Focus in Grade 1

Teaching with Curriculum Focal Points

The Teaching with Curriculum Focal Points series consists of grade-level publications designed to support teachers, supervisors, and coordinators as they begin the discussion of a more focused curriculum across and within prekindergarten through grade 8, as presented in *Curriculum Focal Points for Prekindergarten through Grade 8 Mathematics*.

	ISBN #	NCTM stock #
Focus in Prekindergarten	978-0-87353-644-8	13626
Focus in Kindergarten	978-0-87353-645-5	13627
Focus in Grade 2	Coming Fall 2010	
Focus in Pre-K–2	978-0-87353-624-0	13486
Focus in Grade 3	978-0-87353-625-7	13487
Focus in Grade 4	978-0-87353-627-1	13490
Focus in Grade 5	978-0-87353-614-1	13437
Focus in Grades 3–5	978-0-87353-609-7	13395
Focus in Grade 6	978-0-87353-648-6	13630
Focus in Grade 7	978-0-87353-649-3	13631
Focus in Grade 8	978-0-87353-650-9	13632
Focus in Grades 6–8	978-0-87353-618-9	13465

Please visit www.nctm.org/catalog for details and ordering information.

T 15435

Focus in Grade 1

Teaching with Curriculum Focal Points

Planning and Writing Team

Karen C. Fuson, *Chair, Northwestern University (Professor Emerita)*

Douglas H. Clements, *University at Buffalo, State University of New York*

Sybilla Beckmann, *University of Georgia*

NCTM

NATIONAL COUNCIL OF
TEACHERS OF MATHEMATICS

Library of Congress Cataloging-in-Publication Data

Fuson, Karen C.
    Focus in grade 1 : teaching with curriculum focal points / planning and writing team, Karen C. Fuson,
Douglas H. Clements, Sybilla Beckman.
        p. cm.
Includes bibliographical references and index.
ISBN 978-0-87353-646-2
    1.   Mathematics—Study and teaching (Primary)—Standards—United States. 2. Education, Primary—
    Curricula—Standards—United States. 3. Curriculum planning—Standards—United States. I. Clements, Douglas H.
    II. Beckman, Sybilla. III. Title. IV. Title: Focus in grade one.
    QA135.6.F868 2010
    372.7—dc22

2010005418

The National Council of Teachers of Mathematics is a public voice of mathematics education,
supporting teachers to ensure equitable mathematics learning of the highest quality for all students
through vision, leadership, professional development, and research.

Printed in the United States of America

Contents

3. Geometry, Spatial Reasoning, and Measurement

Contents — Continued

On September 12, 2006, the National Council of Teachers of Mathematics released *Curriculum Focal Points for Prekindergarten through Grade 8 Mathematics: A Quest for Coherence* to encourage discussions at the national, state, and district levels on the importance of designing a coherent elementary mathematics curriculum focusing on the important mathematical ideas at each grade level. The natural question that followed the release of *Curriculum Focal Points* was "How do we translate this view of a focused curriculum into the classroom?"

Focus in Grade 1, one in a series of grade-level publications, is designed to support teachers, supervisors, and coordinators as they begin the discussion of a more focused curriculum across and within prekindergarten through eighth grade, as presented in *Curriculum Focal Points.* Additionally, teacher educators should find it useful as a vehicle for exploring mathematical ideas and curriculum issues involving the first grade mathematics curriculum with their preservice teachers.

The members of the planning and writing team, all active leaders in mathematics education and professional development, created this grade-level book as a framework for individual or group experiences in which teachers deepen their understanding of the mathematical ideas they will be teaching. This book describes and illustrates learning paths for the mathematical concepts and skills of each grade 1 Focal Point, including powerful representational supports for teaching and learning that can facilitate understanding, stimulate productive discussions about mathematical thinking, and provide a foundation for fluency with the core ideas. We also discuss common student errors and misconceptions, reasons the errors may arise, and teaching methods or visual representations to address the errors. Because learning paths cut across grades, we have included some discussion of related Focal Points at prekindergarten and kindergarten so that we can describe and clarify prerequisite knowledge in grade 1 that contributes to later understandings.

Whether you are working with your colleagues or individually, we hope you will find the discussions of the learning paths, representations, and lines of reasoning valuable as you plan activities and discussions for your students and as you strive to help your students achieve the depth of understanding of important mathematical concepts necessary for their future success.

—Karen C. Fuson, *Chair*
Douglas H. Clements
Sybilla Beckmann
Grade 1 Planning and Writing Team

As states and local school districts implement more rigorous assessment and accountability systems, teachers often face long lists of mathematics topics or learning expectations to address at each grade level, with many topics repeating from year to year. Lacking clear, consistent priorities and focus, teachers stretch to find the time to present important mathematical topics effectively and in depth.

The National Council of Teachers of Mathematics (NCTM) is responding to this challenge by presenting *Curriculum Focal Points for Prekindergarten through Grade 8 Mathematics: A Quest for Coherence*. Building on *Principles and Standards for School Mathematics* (NCTM 2000), this new publication is offered as a starting point in a dialogue on what is important at particular levels of instruction and as an initial step toward a more coherent, focused curriculum in this country.

The writing team for *Curriculum Focal Points for Prekindergarten through Grade 8 Mathematics* consisted of nine members, with at least one university-level mathematics educator or mathematician and one pre-K–8 classroom practitioner from each of the three grade bands (pre-K–grade 2, grades 3–5, and grades 6–8). The writing team examined curricula from multiple states and countries as well as a wide array of researchers' and experts' writings in creating a set of focal points for pre-K–grade 8 mathematics.

On behalf of the Board of Directors, we thank everyone who helped make this publication possible.

Cathy Seeley
President, 2004–2006
National Council of Teachers of Mathematics

Francis (Skip) Fennell
President, 2006–2008
National Council of Teachers of Mathematics

Members of the Curriculum Focal Points for Grades PK–8 Writing Team

Jane F. Schielack, *Chair,* Texas A&M University, College Station, Texas
Sybilla Beckmann, University of Georgia, Athens, Georgia
Randall I. Charles, San José State University (emeritus), San José, California
Douglas H. Clements, University at Buffalo, State University of New York, Buffalo, New York
Paula B. Duckett, District of Columbia Public Schools (retired), Washington, D.C.
Francis (Skip) Fennell, McDaniel College, Westminster, Maryland
Sharon L. Lewandowski, Bryant Woods Elementary School, Columbia, Maryland
Emma Treviño, Charles A. Dana Center, University of Texas at Austin, Austin, Texas
Rose Mary Zbiek, The Pennsylvania State University, University Park, Pennsylvania

Staff Liaison
Melanie S. Ott, National Council of Teachers of Mathematics, Reston, Virginia

The National Council of Teachers of Mathematics would like to thank Janet Zaccierello, De Ann Huinker, and Henry S. Kepner Jr. for thoughtful and helpful comments on drafts of the manuscript. Special thanks are due to Francis (Skip) Fennell for initiating the project and for his enthusiastic support and encouragement, and to Henry S. Kepner Jr. for continuing to carry the Focal Points torch with equal dedication and support.

The final product reflects the editorial expertise of Ann M. Butterfield, NCTM senior editor, and the design expertise of Randy White, NCTM production manager.

Purpose of This Guide

Your first question when looking at NCTM's Curriculum Focal Points might be "How can I use NCTM's Focal Points with the local and state curriculum I am expected to teach?" The intent of this guide is to help instructional leaders and classroom teachers build focus into the curriculum that they are expected to teach through connecting related ideas and prioritizing topics of emphasis at each grade level. NCTM's Curriculum Focal Points documents are not intended to be a national curriculum but have been developed to help bring more consistency to mathematics curricula across the country. Collectively, they constitute a framework of how curriculum might be organized at each grade level, prekindergarten through grade 8. They are also intended to help bring about discussion within and across states and school districts about the important mathematical ideas to be taught at each grade level. Because of the current variation among states' curricula, the Curriculum Focal Points are not likely to match up perfectly with any state curriculum. This volume, a guide to the Focal Points for grade 1, explores the mathematics that is emphasized in a focused curriculum. Major aspects of the kindergarten Focal Points are summarized here to provide background for grade 1. See *Focus in Kindergarten* (NCTM 2010) for more details about the kindergarten Focal Points.

Purpose of Curriculum Focal Points

The mathematics curriculum in the United States has often been characterized as a "mile wide and an inch deep." Many topics are studied each year—often reviewing much that was covered in previous years—and little depth is added each time the topic is addressed. In contrast, higher performing countries tend to select a few fundamental topics each year and develop them in greater depth. In addition, because education has always been locally controlled in the United States, learning expectations can significantly differ by state and local school systems.

In the 1980s, the National Council of Teachers of Mathematics (NCTM) began the process of bringing about change to school mathematics programs, particularly with the first document to outline standards in mathematics, titled *Curriculum and Evaluation Standards for School Mathematics* (NCTM 1989). This document provided major direction to states and school districts in developing their curricula. NCTM's *Principles and Standards for School Mathematics* (2000) further elaborated the ideas of the 1989 Standards, outlining learning expectations in the grade bands of pre-K–2, 3–5, 6–8, and 9 12. *Principles and Standards* also highlighted six principles, which included the Curriculum Principle, to offer guidance for developing mathematics programs. The Curriculum Principle emphasized the need to link with, and build on, mathematical ideas as students progress through the grades, deepening their mathematical knowledge over time.

> *A curriculum is more than a collection of activities: It must be coherent, focused on important mathematics, and well articulated across the grades.*
>
> —The Curriculum Principle, *Principles and Standards for School Mathematics*

NCTM's *Curriculum Focal Points for Prekindergarten through Grade 8 Mathematics: A Quest for Coherence* (2006) is the next step in helping states and local districts refocus their curricula. It provides an example of a focused and coherent curriculum in prekindergarten through grade 8 by identifying the most important mathematical topics or "Focal Points" at each grade level. The Focal Points are not discrete topics to be taught and checked off, but rather a cluster of related knowledge, skills, and concepts. By organizing and prioritizing curriculum and instruction in grades pre-K–8 around Focal Points at each grade level, teachers can foster more cumulative learning of mathematics by students, and students' work in the later grades will build on and deepen what they learned in the earlier grades. Organizing mathematics content in this way will help ensure a solid mathematical foundation for high school mathematics and beyond.

Impact of Focal Points on Curriculum, Instruction, and Assessment

Significant improvement can be made in the areas of curriculum, instruction, and assessment by identifying Focal Points at each grade level. At the curriculum level, Focal Points will allow for more rigorous and in-depth study of important mathematics at each grade level. This rigor will translate to a more meaningful curriculum that students can understand and apply, thereby ensuring students' learning and an increase in students' achievement. At the instructional level, Focal Points will allow teachers to more fully know the core topics they are responsible for teaching. Professional development can also be tailored to deepen teachers' knowledge of these Focal Points and connect these ideas in meaningful ways. Assessments can be designed that truly measure students' mastery of core topics rather than survey a broad range of disparate topics, thus allowing for closer monitoring of students' development. At the classroom assessment level, having a smaller number of essential topics will help teachers determine what their students have learned and provide sufficient time to ensure that these topics have been learned deeply enough to use and build on in subsequent years. If state assessments are more focused as well, more detailed information can be gathered for districts and schools on areas for improvement.

Using This Guide in Study Groups or Learning Communities

Many teachers tell us that they did not have an opportunity in school to build sufficient understanding of many topics that they now teach. Therefore our discussion of the grade 1 Focal Points is detailed enough for teachers to begin building such understanding. We suggest that teachers form study groups (such as those in lesson study, mathematics circles, or other learning communities) to read and discuss parts of this volume, to work together to build a deeper understanding of the Focal Points topics, and to plan how to develop such understanding with students by adapting as needed their present grade 1 teaching and learning materials. A helpful approach for other teacher working groups has been to share students' insights and questions and to look at students' work to understand different ways that students are solving problems, to address errors, and to help move students forward in a learning path that fosters both understanding and fluency. Because teachers' lives are busy and demanding, they are better served by concentrating on small chunks of this volume at a time and working through them deeply rather than trying to do too much and getting discouraged. Teachers' learning, like students' learning, is a continuing process, but one that can be very rewarding.

Bringing Focus into the Classroom: Classrooms That Build Understanding and Fluency

Students cannot build understanding in a classroom in which the teacher does all the talking and explaining. Pedagogical principles for classrooms that do help students build understanding are outlined in *Principles and Standards for School Mathematics* (NCTM 2000) and the National Research Council reports *Adding It Up* (Kilpatrick, Swafford, and Findell 2001) and *How Students Learn: Mathematics in the Classroom* (Donovan and Bransford 2005). A learning-path pedagogical perspective that coordinates the principles from these three sources is outlined in Fuson and Murata (2007). This approach also integrates understanding and fluency. In such an approach, teachers create a nurturing, meaning-making "math talk" community in which students discuss their mathematical thinking and help one another clarify their own thinking, understand and overcome errors, and describe the method they use to solve a problem. Teachers and students assist everyone's learning by coaching one another during such math talk and during problem solving if needed. Teachers and students model, structure and clarify, instruct or explain, question, and give feedback.

Using mathematical drawings

The use of mathematical drawings during problem solving and explaining of mathematical thinking helps listeners understand the thinking and the explanation of the speaker. The use of mathematical drawings during homework and classwork helps the teacher understand students' thinking and thus provides continual assessment to guide instruction as the teacher addresses issues that arise in such drawings (e.g., errors or interesting mathematical thinking). Mathematical drawings do not show situational details of the real object; such drawings should be done in art class, not in mathematics class. Mathematical drawings focus on the mathematically important features and relationships, such as the quantity and operations, and can use small circles or other simple shapes. These representations can evolve into schematic numerical drawings that show relations or operations. Throughout this volume, we use mathematical drawings that can be produced and understood by students.

Learning phases

The learning-path pedagogical perspective that integrates understanding and fluency has four phases for each new topic area. The phases begin by building understanding and then move to emphasizing fluency. For each new mathematics topic, teachers—

a) begin by eliciting students' thinking;

b) teach research-based mathematically desirable and accessible methods that reflect the standard algorithmic approach, discuss and repair errors, and ensure that standard approaches are discussed and related to methods that students understand;

c) help students achieve fluency with a general method while continuing to build relationships and understanding; and

d) continue cumulative practice occasionally all year so that students remember what they have learned.

Moving to mathematically desirable methods

Eliciting students' thinking when beginning each new topic is important so that the teacher can build on that thinking and modify and extend it as needed. The teacher needs to emphasize sense making by all participants through all four of the phases above. Although some students will develop fairly advanced methods, allowing too much time for students to "invent" methods can leave less-advanced students doing a primitive method that is slow and perhaps error prone for an extended period. Mathematically desirable methods that are generalizable to larger numbers and that use important mathematical aspects of the quantities involved (for example, hundreds, tens, and ones) need to be introduced if they have not arisen from other students or from the instructional program. These methods should also be accessible to students and build on their ways of thinking. We discuss such methods for the grade 1 Focal Points. These methods enable everyone to use a method that they can understand and explain but that is also mathematically desirable.

The standard algorithmic approach

The Focal Points specify topics for which students should achieve fluency with the standard algorithm. By this phrase, mathematicians mean the *standard algorithmic approach* that involves certain basic steps and not the specific ways in which numerals are written to show these steps. So, for example, multidigit addition and subtraction involve two major steps: adding or subtracting like units (tens and tens or ones and ones) and regrouping if needed (making a new ten when adding and ungrouping a ten to make 10 ones when subtracting). These concepts are discussed and exemplified in the section on multidigit adding. Simpler and more complex ways to write this same standard algorithmic approach for addition are presented later. Each way has disadvantages and advantages, and students can identify and discuss these.

Adding It Up (Kilpatrick, Swafford, and Findell 2001) clarified that in fact no such thing as *the* standard algorithm exists. Many different algorithms (systematic methods of repeated steps for carrying out a computation) have been used over time in the United States, and many different algorithms are used presently in other countries. Students from other countries may bring such written methods into a classroom in the United States. Students from the United States will bring the current common methods from home. All such methods need to be discussed and related to mathematical drawings or other quantities so that all methods can be understood. A student should be allowed to use any method that is mathematically desirable and that the student can explain. Mathematically desirable methods use the standard algorithmic approach and therefore meet any state goal that requires use of the standard algorithm (this phrase is just another way to say the standard algorithmic approach). Some mathematics programs suggest that students not use the standard algorithm because it often involves a complex way of writing steps, but this method will come from some homes and does need to be included in the class discussion. This view emphasizes that the steps and the meanings underlying the algorithm are the important features, and understanding these—and why they work—is a major focus of the work with the algorithm.

Conceptual prerequisites

Helping all students move rapidly to a mathematically desirable and accessible method requires that they have the conceptual prerequisites for such methods. The teacher may need to build in these prerequisites in advance before introducing the topic. We summarize important prerequisites for the grade 1 Focal Points here. See *Focus in Kindergarten* (NCTM 2010) for more details about these prerequisites that need to be developed in kindergarten.

In-depth instructional conversations

During the second learning phase, when multiple methods are discussed and introduced, the math talk should be an instructional conversation that continually focuses on moving students through learning paths to more-advanced understandings. Such discussions need to identify commonalities and differences and advantages and disadvantages across methods. Discussions should involve respectful listening to the explanations of others; students need to learn not to interrupt to take one's turn or explain without listening to the other explanations. Often a fruitful approach is to go on after two or three explanations to have everyone solve and explain another problem; good methods can be explained on a subsequent problem. Another helpful tactic is to have many students solve at the board while the rest of the class solves at their seats, or use some other method of presenting students' solution methods without wasting class time while students sit doing nothing as other students write their methods on the board.

Many students can understand, relate, and build to fluency more than one method. Thus, they are also following a learning path to increased understanding and fluency even if they began with knowing just one method.

During the third phase of focusing on fluency, the number of problems per class period will increase and the amount of class discussion will decrease. But issues will still arise that need to be discussed and clarified, and the focus on making sense continues during all phases.

Differentiating instruction within whole-class activities

This pedagogical approach, which comes from major national reports and from the NCTM Process Standards, actually allows teachers to differentiate instruction within whole-class activities. Such differentiation is possible because the whole range of student methods from less advanced to more advanced is described by students or introduced by the program or by the teacher. The teacher (and, ideally, the mathematics program) helps students move through a learning path to fluency with a mathematically desirable and accessible method or to relating and using two or more such methods.

Learning similarities across number and operations, geometry, and measurement

Mathematics is powerful because it unifies a wide variety of situations and applies to many different examples. To tap into the power of mathematics, children must *mathematize* the situations they encounter. For example, children mathematize when they notice and count that there are three squirrels rather than just "some squirrels," when they see that they need to get exactly four more spoons so that everyone will have one, or when they observe that a paper napkin is in the shape of a square but a tissue is not. To mathematize is to focus on the mathematical aspects of a situation and then to formulate that situation in mathematical terms; it is a means for children to deepen, extend, elaborate, and refine their thinking as they explore ideas and lines of reasoning. When children mathematize their experiences, they solve problems; they reason and communicate their reasoning; they represent ideas using objects, drawings, written symbols, or internal visualization; and they connect ideas. When children mathematize, they use mathematics to help make sense of the world, and they also build their knowledge of mathematics itself. They develop and use special "math eyes" that see the mathematics in the world, and they learn the mathematics language that describes those mathematical aspects.

In addition to the general processes of representing, reasoning, communicating, connecting, and problem solving, specific mathematical reasoning processes also exist that are important across all topics in mathematics and that mathematics instruction should help children develop. These processes are—

- unitizing—finding or creating a unit, such as joining 10 ones to create a unit of ten or recognizing that a repeating pattern ababab... is created by repeating the unit ab;
- decomposing and composing, such as putting six triangles together in a special way to make a hexagon, decomposing a square into two triangles, or decomposing seven toy dinosaurs into a group of five and a group of two;
- relating and ordering, such as putting a collection of sticks in order by length or determining which collection of bears has more by matching; and
- looking for patterns and structures and organizing information, such as noticing that seven and three more must be the same amount as three and seven more or sorting a collection of shapes according to how many sides the shapes have.

Effective Teaching-Learning Practices

Aspects of effective teaching-learning practices are outlined in table 1.1. Most of them have been mentioned in the foregoing. They are summarized to emphasize that the need for focused mathematics teaching time goes well beyond a single approach. It does not mean all teacher showing and telling or an emphasis on worksheets. Parts A and B of table 1.1 emphasize the two ongoing vital roles of teachers:

A. expect and support children's ability to make meaning and mathematize the real world, and

B. create a nurturing and helping math-talk community.

Part C reiterates the need for a teacher to lead the class through a research-based learning path based on children's thinking, as outlined in tables 2.1 and 3.1 and discussed in this book. An important part of such learning paths is that they provide repeated meaningful experience with core concepts so that young children can truly learn in depth. Such learning requires focusing more deeply on fewer topics, a crucial aspect of the Focal Point goals presented and discussed here.

Table 1.1
Effective Teaching-Learning Practices

A. The teacher expects and supports children's ability to make meaning and mathematize the real world by—
  - providing *settings that connect* mathematical language and symbols to quantities and to actions in the world,
  - *leading children's attention* across these crucial aspects to help them see patterns and make connections, and
  - *supporting repeated experiences* that give children time and opportunity to build their ideas, develop understanding, and increase fluency.

B. The teacher creates a nurturing and helping *math-talk community*—
  - within which to *elicit thinking* from students, and
  - to help students *explain and help* each other explain and solve problems.

C. For each big mathematics topic, the teacher leads the class through a *research-based learning path* based on children's thinking. Doing so allows the teacher to differentiate instruction within whole-class activities. This path provides the repeated experiences that young children need.

D. Children need to relate activities with real three-dimensional objects or math drawings to mathematical symbols to *support meaning making with written mathematical symbols.*

Organization of This Book

The rest of this book is in three sections. The original brief Focal Points for grade 1 appear first, and then the detailed goals in tables 2.1 and 3.1 begin the next two sections. The language in the detailed tables sometimes has been modified from the original Focal Point language to be clearer. The final section briefly revisits grade 1 mathematizing and mathematical processes across the Focal Points.

The three grade 1 Focal Points and their connections are reproduced on the following page.

Curriculum Focal Points and Connections for Grade 1

The set of three Curriculum Focal Points and related Connections for mathematics in grade 1 follow. These topics are the recommended content emphases for this grade level. It is essential that these Focal Points be addressed in contexts that promote problem solving, reasoning, communication, making connections, and designing and analyzing representations.

Grade 1 Curriculum Focal Points	Connections to the Focal Points
Number and Operations and *Algebra:* **Developing understandings of addition and subtraction and strategies for basic addition facts and related subtraction facts**	***Number and Operations*** and *Algebra:* Children use mathematical reasoning, including ideas such as commutativity and associativity and beginning ideas of tens and ones, to solve two-digit addition and subtraction problems with strategies that they understand and can explain. They solve both routine and nonroutine problems.
Children develop strategies for adding and subtracting whole numbers on the basis of their earlier work with small numbers. They use a variety of models, including discrete objects, length-based models (e.g., lengths of connecting cubes), and number lines, to model "part-whole," "adding to," "taking away from," and "comparing" situations to develop an understanding of the meanings of addition and subtraction and strategies to solve such arithmetic problems. Children understand the connections between counting and the operations of addition and subtraction (e.g., adding two is the same as "counting on" two). They use properties of addition (commutativity and associativity) to add whole numbers, and they create and use increasingly sophisticated strategies based on these properties (e.g., "making tens") to solve addition and subtraction problems involving basic facts. By comparing a variety of solution strategies, children relate addition and subtraction as inverse operations.	*Measurement* and *Data Analysis:* Children strengthen their sense of number by solving problems involving measurements and data. Measuring by laying multiple copies of a unit end to end and then counting the units by using groups of tens and ones supports children's understanding of number lines and number relationships. Representing measurements and discrete data in picture and bar graphs involves counting and comparisons that provide another meaningful connection to number relationships.
Number and Operations: **Developing an understanding of whole number relationships, including grouping in tens and ones**	*Algebra:* Through identifying, describing, and applying number patterns and properties in developing strategies for basic facts, children learn about other properties of numbers and operations, such as odd and even (e.g., "Even numbers of objects can be paired, with none left over"), and 0 as the identity element for addition.
Children compare and order whole numbers (at least to 100) to develop an understanding of and solve problems involving the relative sizes of these numbers. They think of whole numbers between 10 and 100 in terms of groups of tens and ones (especially recognizing the numbers 11 to 19 as 1 group of ten and particular numbers of ones). They understand the sequential order of the counting numbers and their relative magnitudes and represent numbers on a number line.	
Geometry: **Composing and decomposing geometric shapes**	
Children compose and decompose plane and solid figures (e.g., by putting two congruent isosceles triangles together to make a rhombus), thus building an understanding of part-whole relationships as well as the properties of the original and composite shapes. As they combine figures, they recognize them from different perspectives and orientations, describe their geometric attributes and properties, and determine how they are alike and different, in the process developing a background for measurement and initial understandings of such properties as congruence and symmetry.	

Reprinted from *Curriculum Focal Points for Prekindergarten through Grade 8 Mathematics: A Quest for Coherence* (Reston, Va.: National Council of Teachers of Mathematics, 2006, p. 13).

Overview

The topic of number and operations has three major components: the number core, the relations core, and the operations core.

- The *number core* focuses on four components:
  - Seeing cardinality (seeing how many there are)
  - Knowing the number-word list (one, two, three, four, etc.)
  - One-to-one counting correspondences when counting
  - Written number symbols (1, 2, 3, etc.)
- The *relations core* concerns finding the relationship between two groups of objects or two numbers: Is one of these more than, or less than, or equal to the other?
- The *operations core* involves adding or subtracting two groups of objects or numbers to make a third.

Each of these is discussed more fully in table 2.1.

Table 2.1

Progression of Ideas about Number and Operations (and Algebra from Kindergarten On)

Kindergarten	Grade 1	Grade 2
The Number Core	**The Number Core**	**The Number Core**
Integrate all core components for teen numbers (10 to 19) to see a ten and some ones in teen numbers (e.g., 18 = 10 + 8) and relate 10 ones to 1 ten. Extend the core components: say the tens list 10, 20, …, 100 and count to 100 by ones, count up to twenty-five things in a row with effort, read and write 1 to 19.	See, say, count, draw, and write tens units and ones units from 1 to 100, seeing and counting the groups of ten both as decades (ten, twenty, thirty, …) and as tens (1 ten, 2 tens, 3 tens, …).	See, say, count, draw, and write hundreds units, tens units, and ones units from 1 to 1,000; use place-value terms in explaining multidigit addition and subtraction.
The Relations (More Than/Less Than) Core	**The Relations (More Than/Less Than) Core**	**The Relations (More Than/Less Than) Core**
Show comparing situations with objects or in a drawing, and match or count to find out *which is more* and *which is less* for two numbers ≤ 10. Use = and ≠ symbols for groups of things, numerals, and pictures of fingers.	Solve additive comparison word problems that ask "How many more (less) is one group than another?" for two numbers ≤ 18 by counting or matching with objects or drawings or by knowing numerical relationships (such word problems describe relations between two numbers more precisely: the difference is now involved). Use the words *more/fewer-less* and > and < to compare numbers to 10 and use the concepts of tens and ones developed in the number core and multiunit objects or math drawings to compare numbers to 100.	Use the words *more/fewer-less* and > and < to compare numbers to 1,000 using knowledge of hundreds, tens, and ones.

(Continued on next page)

Table 2.1 (Continued)

Progression of Ideas about Number and Operations (and Algebra from Kindergarten On)

The Operations (Addition/Subtraction) Core	The Operations (Addition/Subtraction) Core	The Operations (Addition/Subtraction) Core
Use objects or fingers or pictures or math drawings to solve change-plus, change-minus, and put-together/take-apart situation problems and also such word, oral number, and written symbolic problems with totals ≤ 10. Learn to decompose 3, 4, 5 into partners; work on decomposing 6 and 7 (e.g., 6 = 5 + 1, 6 = 4 + 2, 6 = 3 + 3, 6 = 2 + 4, 6 = 1 + 5); and see equations with one number on the left and the partners (addends) on the right.	Use objects or fingers or math drawings and equations to solve change-plus, change-minus, and put-together/take-apart situation problems with all unknowns and also such word, oral number, and written symbolic problems with addends from 1 to 9. Pose as well as solve such problems. After working with additive comparison situations and word problems (see the relations core above), mix all types of word problems. Learn to decompose numbers from 3 to 10 into partners (e.g., 10 = 9 + 1, 10 = 8 + 2, 10 = 7 + 3, 10 = 6 + 4, 10 = 5 + 5) and use these relationships to relate addition and subtraction in problem situations, to add and subtract quickly for totals ≤ 6, and to build the prerequisite knowledge for addition and subtraction strategies. Count on for addition problems with totals ≤ 18. Think of subtraction as finding an unknown addend (e.g., think of and rewrite 14 − 8 = ? as 8 + ? = 14). Count on fluently and accurately to find an unknown addend. Work with derived-fact strategies such as make-a-ten and doubles +1 or −1. Give unknown totals or unknown addends (including for subtraction) quickly for totals ≤ 6. Use the concepts of tens and ones developed in the number core and use multiunit objects or math drawings to add and subtract tens and ones (e.g., 60 + 3) and tens and tens (e.g., 40 + 20) and to add two-digit numbers and ones (e.g., 58 + 6) and 2 two-digit numbers starting with problems requiring regrouping (e.g., 38 + 26) (do not do such subtraction problems with or without regrouping). Relate mathematics drawings to written number (symbolic) work.	Develop fluency in solving all types of addition and subtraction word problems (change-plus, change-minus, put-together/take-apart, and comparison situations) with all unknowns. Solve two-step problems and problems with extra information or not enough information, using all types of word problems with all unknowns for addends 1 to 9. Pose as well as solve such problems. Use partners of single-digit numbers to understand and use partners of decades and of hundreds (e.g., 100 = 90 + 10, 100 = 80 + 20, 100 = 70 + 30, 100 = 60 + 40, 100 = 50 + 50). Develop fluency with addition facts and related subtraction facts: Use level 2 (counting on) or level 3 (derived-fact) solution procedures or rapid known facts to solve additions and subtractions and to solve single-digit additions and subtractions within multidigit problems. Develop fluency with addition and subtraction to 1,000: Use the concepts of hundreds, tens, and ones developed in the number core and multiunit objects or math drawings to add and subtract two-digit numbers to 100 requiring regrouping, then problems to 200 with and without regrouping, and then pairs of all sizes of numbers to 1,000 including problems given horizontally. Relate steps with objects or drawings to steps with written numbers, then later do written number work with understanding without objects or drawings. Solve change-plus, change-minus, put-together/take-apart, and comparison situations with all unknowns using numeric math drawings or situation equations and numeric methods for totals to 200 and later for totals to 1,000. Pose as well as solve such problems. Relate word problems and numerical work continually.

The Number Core

The number core developed in preschool and kindergarten

The number core for kindergarten is outlined in the table 2.1 and discussed in detail in the book *Focus in Kindergarten* (NCTM 2010). A brief summary is included in this book to foster understanding of what children with adequate learning experiences have been able to learn. Children without such experiences will need extra time and support at school and at home at the beginning of grade 1 to build this knowledge. Suggestions for this support are included here in the kindergarten summaries. The number core content for prekindergarten is overviewed in *Focus in Kindergarten* and discussed in more detail in *Focus in Prekindergarten* (NCTM 2010).

Initially the four number core aspects (cardinality, number-word list, counting correspondences, and written number symbols) are separate. Then children make vital connections. *First,* they connect saying the number-word list with one-to-one correspondence to begin counting objects. Initially, counting is just an activity and does not have cardinal meaning, because young children do not understand that the last word is special, that it tells them the total amount (its cardinality). If a child at this level is asked the question "How many are there?" after she or he has counted, she or he may count again (repeatedly) or give a number word different from the last counted word. A crucial *second step* is connecting counting and cardinality so that the count tells how many there are. This step in the learning path coordinates the first three aspects of the number core. The *third step* connects counting and cardinality in the opposite direction: 4s/pre-Ks come to be able to count out a specified number of objects (e.g., six). Doing so requires that counting be so automatic for them that they have mental capacity to remember the word *six* while they are counting. Therefore, children in grade 1 who cannot yet do this will need lots of practice counting groups of objects or pictures and telling how many there are (see later kindergarten section). Counting can then become fluent enough that they will have mental space to remember the word to which they are counting. A few first graders may also need support to learn the first two steps (see the sidebar "Teaching the Cardinality Principle").

Prekindergarten and kindergarten children also master the relationships among count words, written numbers, and quantities for numbers from 1 to 10. They count or see (perceptually subitize) quantities, relating the quantity to a number word that tells how many there are (the cardinality). They also relate written number symbols to number words and to seen or counted quantities. They begin to see two small quantities and see/know their total; this is called *conceptual subitizing* (e.g., see two and two and say *four*). Five-groups (see figure 2.1) are especially important as a basis for later work with groups of tens, and they relate to fingers and to coins (nickels). Other groups (twos and fours) can also be helpful visualizations.

Teaching the Cardinality Principle

The adult puts out three to seven objects in a row in front of the child each time.

"When you count, the *last* word you say tells you how many things there are. Watch me. One, two, three, four, five, six" (adult counts blocks pointing to each block). "*Six*. There are *six* blocks" (adult gestures in a narrow ellipse over the set of six blocks).

"Watch again." Repeat for five small toy pigs. "When you count, the *last* word you say tells you how many things there are. Watch me. One, two, three, four, five" (adult counts toy pigs, pointing to each pig). "*Five*. There are *five* pigs" (adult gestures in a narrow ellipse over the set of five pigs).

"Watch again." Repeat for seven pennies. "When you count, the *last* word you say tells you how many things there are. Watch me. One, two, three, four, five, six, seven" (adult counts pennies pointing to each penny). "*Seven*. There are *seven* pennies" (adult gestures in a narrow ellipse over the set of seven pennies).

"So the *last* word you say in counting tells you how many things you have.

Now you try it. How many trucks are here?"

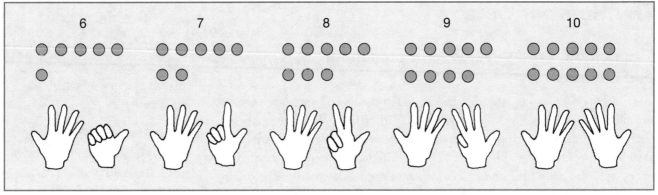

Figure 2.1. Seeing 5-groups that show 6 as 5 + 1, 7 as 5 + 2, 8 as 5 + 3, 9 as 5 + 4, and 10 as 5 + 5

Kindergarten children can consolidate and extend earlier number core experiences in the four aspects so that they—

- see numbers 6 to 9 with a 5-group (dot arrays, fingers) within teen numbers 16 to 19;
- say the number-word list to 100 and say the tens list 10, 20, 30, …, 90, 100;
- count up to twenty-five things in a row with effort and count out *n* things up to twenty;
- read and write numerals 1 to 19.

The major new advance in kindergarten is the crucial step described in two National Research Council reports (Kilpatrick, Swafford, and Findell 2001; Cross, Woods, and Schweingruber 2009): Kindergarten children integrate all the core components of number to see that teen numbers are made up of a ten and some ones. Before discussing this major step, we need to review the difficulties English number words make for understanding teen numbers and numbers from 20 to 100.

Difficulties in English number words for 11 to 19

The first ten number words are arbitrary in most languages. But then most languages begin to have patterns that make the number words easier to learn. English has a partial pattern for words from eleven to nineteen, but this pattern is marred by irregularities. These problematic issues are summarized in table 2.2 and listed below. For simplicity we will call these numbers *teen* numbers even though not all number words for these numbers have the *-teen* suffix.

- The partial pattern is to say one of the first nine counting words and add *-teen* to it (the *-teen* means *ten*), as in *fourteen, sixteen, seventeen, eighteen, nineteen*.
- However, the first two "teen" words (*eleven, twelve*) do not have the *-teen* ending.
- The third and fifth words have modified the number below ten so that it may not be recognizable: *thirteen* instead of *threeteen* and *fifteen* instead of *fiveteen*.

Children frequently see and use the *-teen* structure before they learn the exceptions, as in this diary example for a child aged three years two months: *"Eight, nine, ten, eleventeen, twelveteen, thirteen."* Parents and teachers can discuss these irregularities.

- "What would be better number words than *eleven* and *twelve?* (*oneteen* and *twoteen*)
- "What would be clearer to say than *fifteen?*" (*fiveteen*)
- "Yes, it is harder to have some of the number words we have, but we need to use them or other people will not understand us."

Many children skip over fifteen even when they can say the end of the teens ("sixteen, seventeen, eighteen, nineteen") correctly. This may be because it is in the middle and because it is irregular. So parents and teachers may need to focus children's attention and work particularly on the word *fifteen*.

Table 2.2
Difficulties in Learning English Words from 1 to 100

English number words for the first four places name the values for the third and fourth places from the right (*hundred* and *thousand*). But there are many irregularities for the second place, where we never say *ten* but only say *-teen* or *-ty*. So 2222 is *two thousand two hundred twenty two*. In a totally regular named-value system, such as Chinese, Japanese, and related systems, the number would be *two thousand two hundred two ten two one*.

Difficulties in English number words for 10 to 19. These teen words follow the reversals of German languages in which the ones are said before the tens.
a. Written numerals show the ones second, and teen words say them first (if at all): 18 but eighteen.
b. Written numerals do not show that the 1 is really one ten or ten ones. It looks like 1, not 10.
c. The teen words never say *ten*, and only some say *teen*.
d. *Ten* is not *one ten*, *eleven* is not *oneteen*, and *twelve* is not *twoteen*.
   We say *thirteen*, not *threeteen*, and *fifteen*, not *fiveteen*.
   Only *fourteen, sixteen, seventeen, eighteen, nineteen* have any pattern that can relate easily to some ones and a ten, and this pattern is late in the teens.
   This is in contrast to East Asian number words that are said as *ten one, ten two, ten three, ..., ten nine, two ten* (20).
e. The English words for 20 to 100 say the ones second, opposite to the pattern for the teens.
f. There is auditory confusion between teen and decade words: fourteen and forty, sixteen and sixty, seventeen and seventy, and so on.

Difficulties in English number words for 20 to 99. These teen words do not follow the reversals of German languages but do have irregularities.
g. We say *-ty* instead of *ten*: the suffix *-ty* is added to the digit word (one, two, three, etc.) to say 20, 30, ..., 90, but *-ty* does not say *ten* clearly.
h. Four of the earliest decade words are irregular and do not even show this *digit-ty* structure clearly: 10 is said as *ten* not *one ten*, 20 as *twen-ty* (not *two tens* or *two-ty*), 30 as *thir-ty* (not *three tens* or *three-ty*), and 50 as *fif-ty* (not *five tens* or *five-ty*); only 40 (*four-ty*), 60 (*six-ty*), 70 (*seven-ty*), 80 (*eight-ty*), 90 (*nine-ty*) show this structure clearly.

This *ones-before-tens* structure of the teen words is opposite to the *tens-before-ones* structure in the written teen number symbols. We say "four" first in "fourteen" but write 4 second in 14 (1 ten 4 ones). This reversal, and the irregularities listed in the foregoing, make the pattern-finding activity of relating written numerals to teen number words particularly complex for children speaking English. They need help and support to learn to say the teen numbers correctly. These are discussed in the kindergarten number core.

A final difficulty in understanding the meaning of the teens words is that English words do not explicitly say the *ten* that is in the teen number (*teen* does not mean *ten* even to many adults). This anomaly is in contrast with number words in East Asia that are said "ten, ten one, ten two, ten three," and so on, for 10, 11, 12, 13, and so on. Therefore, English-speaking children need particular help seeing the ten inside teen quantities. This is a goal for kindergarten and is discussed more fully after the next section.

Difficulties in English number words for 20 to 99

The *ones-before-tens* structure for English teen numbers comes from German. The same structure is used in German for all numbers from 11 to 99. But English changes for the words from twenty to ninety-nine to the *tens-before-ones* structure. This tens-before-ones structure is the same order in which numerals are written: "twenty" is said first in "twenty-seven," and 2 is written first in 27 (2 tens, 7 ones). So it is easier for children to relate the patterns in the written numerals to English number words from twenty to ninety-nine, a goal for kindergarten. Full understanding of the quantities of tens and ones in these numbers is a goal for grade 1.

The transition in English words from nine to ten is not clear: *ten* just sounds like another word with no special significance. Therefore, at first children often do not stop at twenty-nine but continue to count "twenty-nine, twenty-ten, twenty-eleven, twenty-twelve, twenty-thirteen." This error can be a mixture of not yet understanding that the pattern ends at nine and difficulty stopping the usual counting at nine so as to shift to another decade.

Irregularities in English decade number words complicate saying the number-word list correctly to one hundred (see the bottom of table 2.2). *Forty, sixty, seventy, eighty,* and *ninety* have a regular pattern: The ones word followed by *-ty* (which means ten). But most of the early decade words are irregular:

- *Twenty,* not *twoty* or *two-ten*
- *Thirty,* not *threety* or *three-ten*
- *Fifty,* not *fivety* or *five ten*

As with the teen words, the *ten* is not said explicitly but is said as a different suffix, *-ty.* Therefore, children need to work explicitly with groups of tens and ones to understand these meanings for the decade words from twenty to one hundred as groups of ten.

A kindergarten advance: Seeing/making ten and some ones for a teen number

The various complex relationships that must be understood for this kindergarten advance are shown in figure 2.2. If grade 1 children do not yet have these understandings, it is important for them to be supported to learn them. For many grade

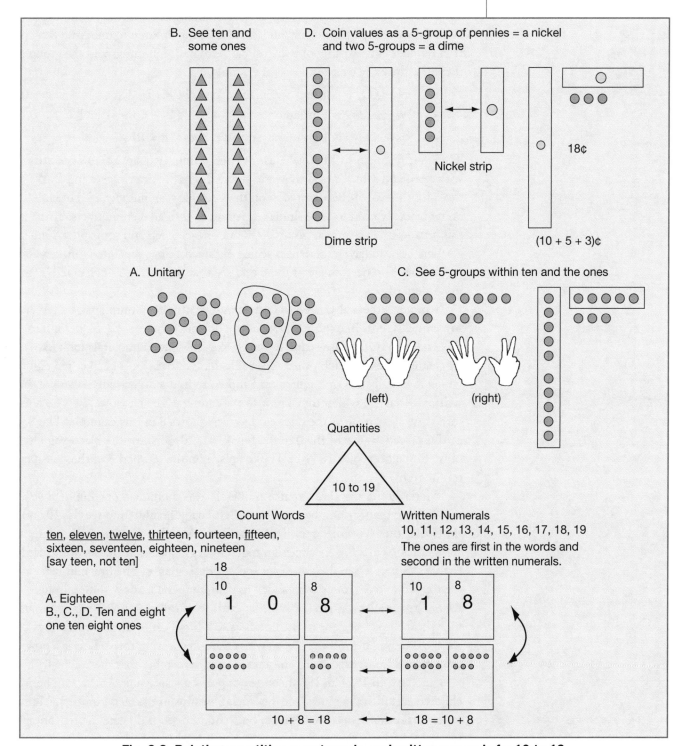

Fig. 2.2. Relating quantities, count words, and written numerals for 10 to 19

1 children, these teen relationships can be learned while learning the grade-level tens and ones relationships for all numbers to 100 (see the later section on this). But special attention does need to be given to the reversed one-before-tens structure in the teens number words. Contrasting pairs of teen and decade words (e.g., *fourteen* and *forty* and 14 and 40) and discussing the patterns in the words and written numerals is helpful.

The first conceptual step toward understanding the tens/ones structure in both the written and spoken symbol systems is for children to understand each teen number as consisting of two groups: 1 group of ten things and the group of the ones (the extra over ten). So, for example,

- *eleven (11)* is 1 group of ten and 1 one (11 = 10 + 1),
- *fourteen (14)* is 1 group of ten and 4 ones (14 = 10 + 4), and
- *eighteen (18)* is 1 group of ten and 8 ones (18 = 10 + 8).

This shift from a quantity made just of ones (a unitary quantity) to a quantity with a ten and some ones is shown in figure 2.2 in the drawings A and B. We focus for the rest of this discussion on the example teen number 18, but children obviously need to have similar experiences with all teen numbers. To create this separation of a unitary group of 18 ones to see a ten and some ones, kindergartners need to have experiences seeing eighteen things separated into ten and eight. They also need to count them and see that the total is not changed by this movement of objects.

Kindergartners also need to understand written teen numbers as a ten and some ones. Cards like those shown at the bottom of figure 2.2 are helpful in this endeavor. Our place-value system makes these teen numerals look like single digits next to each other: "18" looks like "one eight," not like "ten eight," which it actually is. On the tens card shown in figure 2.2, children can see the written ten as 10, which they know as the numeral for the word *ten*. The tens card is twice as wide as the ones card, which shows 8 in this example. The 8 card is placed on top of the 0 in the tens card (10) to show the place-value way of writing eighteen as 18 (1 in the tens place on the left and 8 in the ones place on the right).

Maria Montessori used similar numeral cards more than one hundred years ago. Placing the tiny numbers at the top left enables children to see the 10 and the 8 after they have made the 18 and so helps establish these multiple relationships: 18 is 10 and 8. The circles arranged in 5-groups on the backs of the cards enable children to see the values *ten* and *eight* at a glance. The tiny numbers on the top left and 5-groups were added to plain numeral cards by Fuson in her *Math Expressions* program (2009). The cards were called *secret-code cards* because they show the secret code of the numbers. Children using them say that they can see the 0 hiding behind the 8 even when the 8 is covering the 0. This is a powerful mental image that helps children see and remember that there actually is a 10 and an 8 in 18. This is only one example of a visual support that can help children establish the crucial ten-ones relationships in the teen numbers. Many other versions of visual ways exist to help children see and relate the ten-ones values in the English words, written numerals, and quantities.

Children need to relate the unitary 18 to 10 and 8 in quantities, count words, and written numerals. They need to move from the unitary quantities shown in figure 2.2 in A to the ten and some ones quantities shown in B and, for 16 to 19, also see the 5-groups within the ten and the ones, as in C. Using fingers to show teen numbers (as shown in C in figure 2.1) is also important. Children can flash (open all fingers at once) ten to the left in front of them and then open as many fingers as are in the ones number (8 in 18) and show that to the right in front of them, saying as they make each number, "Ten and eight make eighteen." They can go both directions with the cards, fingers, and words to establish robust relationships. They can show the equation $10 + 8 = 18$ by finger flashes, saying "Ten and eight make eighteen" while someone shows the tens and ones cards 10 and 8 to make 18 (8 goes on top of the 0 in 10). If two sets of cards are used, one student can show the numerals on the fronts of the cards and the other student can show the quantities in 5-groups on the backs of the cards. The other students can show the quantities using finger flashes of a ten and some ones.

Working with the 5-groups within teen numbers enables children who did not have extensive experience with them before or in kindergarten to develop this knowledge and is important for grade 1 and grade 2 understanding. Seeing 6 to 9 as a 5-group and some ones helps pre-K and K children visualize these numbers. These 5-groups are also helpful in visualizing teen numbers. Looking at the backs of the cards at the bottom of figure 2.2, you can see the 10 as two 5-groups and the 8 as a 5-group and 3 ones. This 5-group visualization will be helpful in grades 1 and 2 in discussing the advanced make-a-ten strategy when adding and subtracting. Working with the 5-groups within teen numbers enables first graders who did not have extensive experience with them in kindergarten to develop this knowledge. Children can discuss how the 5-groups relate to their fingers (five fingers on each hand, so six is one hand and one finger on the other hand).

The opposite unitary to ten-and-ones order is also important to practice. "Eighteen is ten and eight" can be said for equations ($18 = 10 + 8$), finger flashes, and both sides of the cards as they begin with 18 and then take off the 8 to see 10 and 8 (in numerals and with dot quantities). Students can lead these practice activities using big cards, fingers, and equations. These triad activities can also be done with quantities in other arrangements, such as those shown in B and C in figure 2.2, or with other visual supports for the numerals $18 = 10$ and 8.

It is important for children to see equations with a single number on the left, as in $18 = 10 + 8$. This exposure will help to avoid the common misconception in algebra that the = is like an arrow that means *becomes* and one number cannot be alone on the left. This issue is discussed further in the sections on operations, where partners of a number are written in the form $5 = 4 + 1$ or $5 = 2 + 3$.

A second, more-advanced understanding is the use of a new unit: a unit of ten. Use of this new ten-unit requires understanding that 10 ones equal 1 ten. This is the first step in the full place-value knowledge to be developed in grade 1: that the numeral in the tens position tells how many tens there are. So the written teen number symbols 18 mean 1 group of ten (1 ten rather than 10 ones) and 8 ones. The arrangements in B, C, and D in figure 2.2 support this shift from the 10 ones as a group to 1 ten as a higher unit because children say that the column of 10 ones looks like the numeral 1 (1 ten). This idea can be started in kindergarten, but it develops more fully in grade 1 with the extension of place value from the teens to ninety-nine. The idea of a tens place (on the left) in which you write the number of tens and a ones place on the right in which you write the number of ones really requires experience with the varied numbers of tens and of ones in the numbers from 20 to 99.

Understanding monetary values

Many states at present require that kindergarten children understand some aspects of money. Some stated goals are beyond what is achievable even for many children who have had strong earlier mathematical experiences. The mathematical aspects of money that are most appropriate are using the ideas of a 5-group and a 10-group that have been developed in kindergarten. Ten pennies make one dime, and five pennies make one nickel. Learning the values of a dime and a nickel are of course particularly complicated because their values are not in the order of the sizes of the coins. In size, a dime is smaller than a penny, but the opposite is true for their value: a penny is less than a dime. Also, there is nothing about the sizes of a penny and a nickel that shows that one nickel equals five pennies. For this reason, it is too difficult to work with these coins alone. Kindergarten children need visual supports that show the values of nickels and dimes in pennies. One such example is shown in figure 2.2 at the top right in D. A nickel strip shows five pennies on one side and one nickel on the other side. A dime strip shows ten pennies on one side and one dime on the other side. Children can use the penny side of these strips to show teen numbers, as in the rightmost drawing in C in figure 2.2: eighteen cents is ten pennies and five pennies and three pennies. Above this drawing on the right of D can be seen 18 cents using the dime strip and nickel strip. The penny strips below in C have been flipped over to show one dime, one nickel, and the three loose pennies that make 18 cents.

Counting mixed collections of dimes, nickels, and pennies requires shifting counts from counting by tens when counting dimes to counting by fives when counting nickels to counting by ones when counting pennies. Such shifts are too complex for many children at this level, especially if children are looking at the coins rather than looking at their values as pennies. Also, any work on the names of the coins (penny, nickel, dime) and on their visual features needs to be related to visually supporting their value as ones, fives, or tens. It is the quantitative values that are mathematically important. Showing 18 cents in pennies using one 10-group, one 5-group, and 3 ones is appropriate for all children in kindergarten. Seeing this value of 18 cents as one dime, one nickel, and three pennies using something like the penny strips that show the quantities is also appropriate. But making 18 cents just with a dime, nickel, and pennies without the intervening visual support of all pennies as in C in figure 2.2 is too difficult for some children in kindergarten and should wait until grade 1. Some children do have experience with money outside of school, and their knowledge will often be above that of their classmates with no such knowledge. Such children can help others who are building the complex triad relationships for money.

Learning the number-word list to 100

Structured learning experiences decrease the time it takes children to learn the pattern of decades to 100 (*ten, twenty, thirty, forty, ..., ninety*) and to learn to use this decade list with the *n-ty to n-ty-nine* pattern. Doing so while looking at the number symbols from 1 to 100 grouped in tens can help reinforce the pattern of these words as meaning groups of ten. Flashing ten fingers as children say each decade word can also begin to build the knowledge of these words as meaning 1 ten, 2 tens, 3 tens, ..., 9 tens. Kindergarten children can discuss patterns they see in the numbers from 20 to 100 and how the *n-ty, n-ty-one, ..., n-ty-nine* pattern relates to the written numerals, for example, for 40, 41, 42, 43, ..., 49.

Written numerals arranged in vertical columns of ten allow children to see the repeating tens number more easily (see figure 2.3) because these tens numbers are visible on the left side of each column (all the 1s are in a column for the teens, all the 2s are in a column for the twenties, etc.). The tens words move along the bottom of such a table and summarize the number of groups of ten so far. It is helpful to have the groups of ten numbers in each column grouped in some obvious way rather than just have the usual hundreds grid in which the groups of ten numbers are not so obvious. Classroom uses of the usual horizontal hundreds grid can just be rote jumps of "to the right is one" and "down is ten" rather than the groups of ten being visually salient or understood at all.

1	11	21	31	41	51	61	71	81	91
2	12	22	32	42	52	62	72	82	92
3	13	23	33	43	53	63	73	83	93
4	14	24	34	44	54	64	74	84	94
5	15	25	35	45	55	65	75	85	95
6	16	26	36	46	56	66	76	86	96
7	17	27	37	47	57	67	77	87	97
8	18	28	38	48	58	68	78	88	98
9	19	29	39	49	59	69	79	89	99
10	20	30	40	50	60	70	80	90	100

Fig. 2.3. Patterns in vertical groups of ten in the numbers to 100

Many kindergarten children will not develop full understanding of the triad relationships among tens and ones quantities, count words, and written numerals. As always, production of the number-word list outruns the other number aspects. But kindergartners can learn the patterns in the count words to one hundred. Doing so in the presence of groups of tens visually and with finger flashes can help children build a foundation for fuller understanding of tens and ones in grade 1. As always with the number-word list, it needs to be very fluent so that children can say it in connection with other actions or thoughts. Children need continued experiences counting by tens and by ones to one hundred even after they can do so accurately alone.

Written work for triads to ten and for teens

Written work including activity sheets is appropriate in kindergarten if it follows up on activities with objects or presents supportive visualizations. Children need practice that builds fluency after related experiences with objects to build mathematical understanding, and they need experience relating symbols for quantities to actual or drawn quantities. This is especially important for the teen written numerals and quantities. Children need to follow up the experiences summarized in figure 2.2 and discussed in the foregoing by seeing and drawing quantities and writing numbers in equations on activity sheets that connect quantities as a ten and some ones and teen equations such as $18 = 10 + 8$.

Pictures, scenes, books about number, and activity sheets need to present quantities clearly. Textbooks or worksheets often present sets that are very messy and hard to see. Layouts often discourage seeing patterns of small numbers (perceptual or conceptual subitizing) and frequently depict collections of objects that are difficult to count. Such complicating factors include embedded or overlapping pictures, complex things or pictures with lots of parts (e.g., detailed animals of different sizes rather than circles or squares), lack of symmetry, and irregular arrangements where it is hard to keep track of what you've already counted (Clements and Sarama 2007). Kindergarten children are still building mental images for numerical quantities. Seeing groupings is important, and groups of five and of ten are especially important at this age.

The number core developed in grade 1

The major step in grade 1 is the extension to deep place-value understanding of numbers to 100 and the use of such understanding in adding and (some) subtracting (discussed in the section on operations). Figure 2.4 shows the aspects of multiunit quantities of tens and ones, number words, and written number marks that children in all countries must learn to understand and connect. The written two-digit numerals look like concatenated single digits (two single digits put next to each other): 79 (seven nine). Nothing shows that the 7 means seven groups of ten. The English count words have a named value system that relates to expanded notation. *Seventy-nine* is of the form 70 (+) 9, so it at least says a unitary value *seventy* followed by a unitary *nine*. But as discussed above, it does not clearly say *7 tens*, as do East Asian languages. Initially, *seventy* means either a counting word after *sixty-nine* and before *seventy-one* or a unitary collection of *seventy* things. English-speaking children need to see groups of tens and of ones and say these quantity names (*7 tens, 9 ones*) to fully understand written place-value symbols and English count words. Making all these connections can take a long time.

Historically many different materials have been used to show groups of ten (e.g., bundled sticks, base-ten blocks, linked cubes in groups of ten, Montessori beads on ten-sticks). For kindergarten, we showed in figure 2.2 materials that moved from unitary collections of teen numbers to a ten and some ones. Such a movement from unitary collections to groups of tens and ones for all two-digit numbers is much messier because it involves so many objects. Even working with tens and ones materials is challenging for some first graders. We show in figure 2.4 math drawings of tens and ones that can follow the use of any tens and ones materials or even replace such use. Children can make such drawings and relate them to written numerals and to equations of values because everything can be done on paper or on the board. Such math drawings made on the board make it easy for everyone in the class to understand the discussion about the quantities and numerals, which can get complex when the math talk is about manipulatives but these cannot be drawn on the board. These math drawings are especially helpful for multidigit addition and subtraction, as will be discussed later. They can be built up by drawing a column of ten ones (with a gap between the top five and bottom five so ten can be seen easily). Then a line segment drawn through these 10 ones groups them into 1 ten. When this meaning is clear, just the stick can be drawn and called a ten-stick or quick-ten, but children still visualize the 10 ones on the ten-stick. To make this process faster, the drawings can be done on dot grids so that children do not have to draw all the circles. The penny strips shown in figure 2.2 can also be the initial groups of 10 ones that are then symbolized by the vertical ten-stick. It is important that children understand that the 10 ones can be shown as a ten-stick when needed. This is not a rote symbol.

As with the teen numerals, some forms of secret-code cards in which the ones can go on top of the 0 in the decade numeral can help children overcome the concatenated single-digit form of written numerals. The small numbers written on the top left corners enable children to see that the 79 is really a 70 and 9. Children come to see the 0 hiding under the 9 so that they deeply understand that 79 is not just a 7 and a 9. Children can write both forms of the expanded notation equations $70 + 9 = 79$ and $79 = 70 + 9$. The first form shows the 70 and 9 coming together to become 79, and the second form shows the 79 coming apart to show 70 and 9. Having ten-sticks and ones in 5-groups on the backs of the cards helps with visualization of the multiunit quantities involved. Both sides of the cards need to be named using quantity words *7 tens 9 ones* as well as the English name *seventy-nine*. Another source of quantity meanings is the group of ten fingers. Children can flash their ten fingers seven times to show *7 tens* and then show *9 ones* on their fingers.

Initially, the transition from one decade to the next is difficult for many children. In counting, they may know that the pattern ends at 9 (e.g., 79) but may just get carried along with the counting momentum and so say things like *seventy-nine, seventy-ten*. In such cases it is helpful to have a student leader or

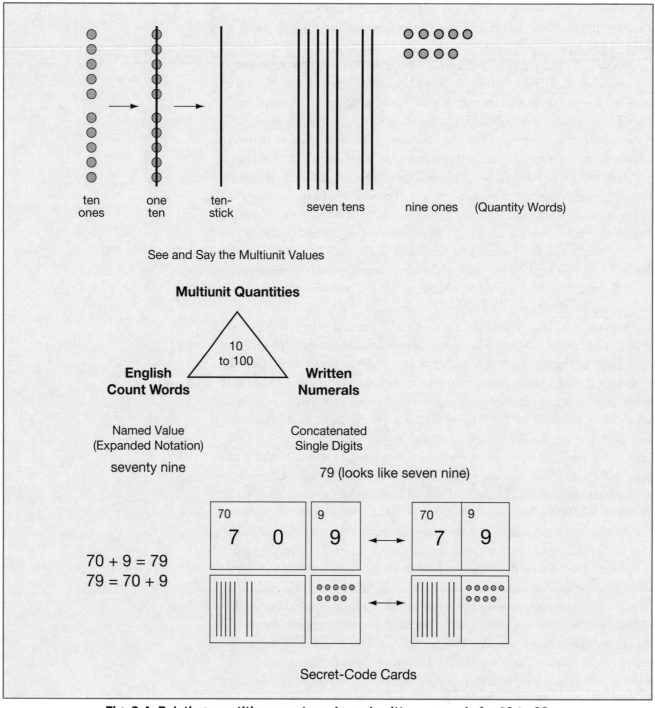

ten ones   one ten   ten-stick   seven tens   nine ones   (Quantity Words)

See and Say the Multiunit Values

Multiunit Quantities

10 to 100

English Count Words

Written Numerals

Named Value (Expanded Notation)

seventy nine

Concatenated Single Digits

79 (looks like seven nine)

$70 + 9 = 79$
$79 = 70 + 9$

Secret-Code Cards

Fig. 2.4. Relating quantities, count words, and written numerals for 10 to 99

teacher raise a hand in a stop motion while all children pause and shift to the new decade. These decade shifts can also be practiced separately in random order. One child says a number ending in 9 (for example, 49), and the rest of the class responds with the next number, the decade word 50.

All the relationships shown in figure 2.4 may need extensive practice. Children can see multiunit quantities and respond with the English name and the quantity word name and make the written numeral with cards and write an equation. Or they can start with an English count word and draw the tens and ones and write the numeral or make it with cards and write an equation. Understanding and fluency require moving among all these relationships. Fuller understanding is developed when children begin to add and subtract two-digit numbers, discussed in the section on operations.

The Relations (More Than/Less Than) Core

The relations (more than/less than) core developed in preschool and kindergarten

The relations core goals require children to learn to perceive, say, discuss, and create the relations *more than, less than,* and *equal to* on two sets. Initially children ages two and three (2s/3s) use general perceptual, length, or density strategies to decide whether one set is *more than, less than,* or *equal to* another set: They decide just by looking overall, or they focus just on the length (see the top example in figure 2.5), or they focus just on how close together the things are. Gradually these are replaced by the more accurate strategies counting and matching. To decide which is more, children age four (4s/pre-Ks) can match the entities in the sets to find out which has leftover entities or they can count both sets and use understandings of *more than/less than* order relations on num-

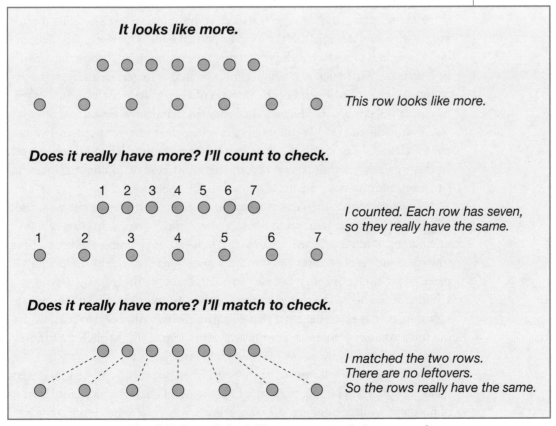

Fig. 2.5. Does it look like more or really have more?

bers (the number said later in counting is more than the number said earlier). They master such situations when both sets are less than or equal to five (≤5). Prekindergartners and kindergartners may need to learn how to match by making line segments (see the bottom of figure 2.5) with their fingers or their eyes to connect pairs of objects, one from each set. They can draw such matching lines if the compared sets are drawn on paper. Then they need to know that the set with any extra objects is *more than* the other set. It is also helpful to match using actual objects, moving the objects so that they are aligned. With objects, it is important to keep the two compared groups visually separate, perhaps by using a piece of string or placing the objects on different colors of paper, so that children know which objects they are comparing.

Kindergarten children make three kinds of advances. They—

- extend their use of matching and counting to sets that are less than or equal to ten (≤ 10),
- count or match pictures or drawings instead of objects, and
- find out and say both relations (more and less) using full sentences, such as "Eight circles are more than six circles. Six circles are less than eight circles."

They also begin the use of symbols for relations by using the symbols for equal (=) and not equal (≠) to relate groups of things, numerals, and pictures (including pictures or drawings of fingers). The symbols less than (<) and greater than (>) are not used until grade 1 because getting their directionality correct is difficult. Children enjoy using the ≠ symbol, and it is a simpler step to decide that two sets are not equal than which is larger/smaller. At this informal level, building meaning for the = and ≠ symbols is the most important issue. Therefore, children can build meanings and practice discriminating these symbols by putting them between various pairs, such as a number and a picture of fingers raised, fingers and pictures of objects, or a number and pictures of objects. In grade 1, the use of mathematical symbols can begin to be restricted to numerals only.

Eventually in grade 1, children begin to see the thirds set potentially present in relational situations, the *difference* between the smaller and the larger set. In this way, relational situations become the third kind of addition/subtraction situation, additive comparison, discussed in the operations core.

Kindergarten children can work within formats that prepare them for use in grade 1 of picture graphs and use in grade 2 of bar graphs. In pairs of rows or columns of ten connected squares, children can draw simple pictures. These rows or columns of pictures can vary only in number (e.g., eight circles compared to six circles), or they can vary in color, shape, or thing being drawn. Children can choose the things or the numbers to compare. The important task then is to make statements that compare the two rows or two columns using full sentences containing *more* or *less,* for example, "Eight circles are more than six circles. Six circles are less than eight circles."

Such sentences will need to be modeled by an adult, and children may need many repetitions to be able to say the full sentence. Gaining such facility is an important foundation for grade 1 comparisons, which are much more complex linguistically because they tell *how many* more/less as well as *which* is more/less. The English linguistic structure is difficult because it does not separate these two ideas. English says "Mary has two more than Bob." The number that tells the difference (here, two) is just inserted into the *which is more/less* sentence. Many children do not even process this number word. They just hear the simpler sentence "Mary has more than Bob." The grade 1 section on comparison problems below discusses this issue more deeply. The important point for kindergartners is that they need to have practice saying which number or quantity is more and which is less without specifying the difference. The distinction between *less* and *fewer* is not important at kindergarten or even at grade 1 (*less* is used for continuous quantities, such as measurements, and for numerals, and *fewer* is used for groups of discrete quantities that can be counted). The vital distinction at both of these grades is between *more* and *less/fewer.*

Children at this level can also prepare for the additive comparison problems at grade 1 by beginning to make two related sets equal. For example, for a row of five above a row of seven, they can be asked to add more to the row of five to make it equal to the row of seven and write their addition 5 + 2. This 2 is the difference between 5 and 7—it is the amount extra that seven has, so such exercises help children begin to see this third quantity in the comparison situation. Grade 1 children will develop this third quantity more fully in the context of comparison word problems and other comparing contexts.

The relations core (more than/less than) developed in grade 1

There are two major advances in the relations core in grade 1. First, instead of just comparing two numbers to find which is more (or less) as described above for kindergarten, first graders can see the *difference* between the smaller and the larger set as a potential third set present in relational situations. This "third set" is actually a subset of the larger set and tells how many more/less. In this way, relational situations become the basis of comparison situations for addition and subtraction (this will be discussed further in the operations core section).

Grade 1 children can also use the concepts of tens and ones developed in the number core and multiunit objects or math drawings to compare numbers to 100. The math drawings allow children to see that even 1 ten is more than 9 (or less). Therefore, such drawings can help with comparisons that children will get wrong if they just look at the numbers and do not think about tens and ones, for example, in comparing 52 and 39. Use of the secret-code cards shown in figure 2.4 can also be helpful. Children can make the quantities 52 and 39 and then take each number apart to see 50 and 2 compared to 30 and 9. If they turn the secret-code cards over, they can also see the drawings in which the 5 tens in 52 are more than 39.

First graders can also use the mathematical symbols > for *more than* and < for *less than*. These symbols can first be used in comparing numbers below ten. Helping children see that the big (wide) part of the symbol always points toward the bigger number increases success in using these symbols.

The Operations (Addition and Subtraction) Core

Overview

In the operations core, children learn to see addition and subtraction situations in the real world by focusing on the mathematical aspects of those situations and making a model of the situation. This process of seeing and focusing on the mathematical aspects and ignoring the nonmathematical aspects (e.g., color) is called *mathematizing*. For addition and subtraction operations, the key mathematical aspects are the number of objects and the actions on the objects (some may be added or subtracted or two groups of objects may be compared). A great deal of research has been conducted about how children come to understand and solve addition and subtraction situations. An accessible review of this research for teachers is *Children's Mathematics: Cognitively Guided Instruction* (Carpenter et al. 1999). This resource also includes a CD that shows children solving various types of problem situations.

The operations core developed in preschool and kindergarten

Types of addition/subtraction situations

Before grade 1, children solve two types of addition/subtraction situations: change plus/change minus and put together/take apart.

Examples of Word-Problem Types in Preschool and Kindergarten

Each of these main types has an addition situation and a related subtraction situation.

Change-plus/change-minus situations:

Addition: change plus:

"One bunny was in the garden. Two bunnies hopped into the garden. How many bunnies are in the garden now?"

Subtraction: change minus:

"Four frogs were sitting on a log. Three frogs jumped off of the log. How many frogs are on the log now?"

Put-together/take-apart situations:

Addition: put together:

"Grammy has one red flower and two blue flowers. How many flowers does she have in all?"

Subtraction (unknown addend): take apart:

"Mom bought three apples. One apple is red. The other apples are yellow. How many yellow apples are there?"

Change situations: change plus and change minus—
- begin with an initial amount (the start),
- then some quantity is added to or taken from that amount (the change),
- creating the final amount (the result).

Collection situations: put together (sometimes called combine) and take apart—
- involve two initial quantities that are put together to make a third quantity (put together), or
- one quantity that is taken apart to make two quantities (take apart).

In story problems at this age, the final amount is the focus of the question in the problem (see example on previous page). In grade 1, change situations can have the start quantity or the change quantity as the unknown number, and collection situations can involve an addend as the unknown.

Solving by modeling

Children solve these problems by modeling the actions or quantities in the situation with objects, fingers, or math drawings (simple drawings using circles or other shapes). The answer is produced as the action is modeled. For take-apart situations in which an addend is unknown, the answer is produced automatically only for problems in which the total is given first, because the total can be made and then the known addend can be separated. To solve all these kinds of problems, children just need to understand the language of the problem and the situation to be able to solve them. Such understanding can be facilitated by acting out situations initially.

Kindergartners also represent situations with equations

The major extension for kindergartners is that addition and subtraction situations are now also represented by written mathematical marks. Teachers relate equations to situations, oral language, and children's solution methods. Initially the teacher writes expressions (3 + 2) and equations (3 + 2 = 5 or 3 + 2 = □). Later, children write expressions and, later still, they write equations. This work with symbols must involve continual relating of real-world situations, mathematical language, expressions and equations, and actions and representations that show the situation and the solution. This builds up meanings for equations. Then children begin to solve equations presented without a story. Children initially tell a story for an equation to continue the meaning making. Then they solve equations without needing to generate a story for each equation because the equations have taken on the situational addition or subtraction meanings.

Children can be helped to understand and remember the meanings of the + and − and = signs in various ways. For the + sign, children can discuss how adding means putting together two groups. They can imagine two groups of things in front of them, put out their two arms and grab the things in those two groups, and bring their arms together so that one arm is horizontal and one is vertical to make a + sign. For the − sign, they can imagine a total in front of them and reach out and take some away by grabbling some of them and pulling them horizontally to the right to take them away, thus making a minus sign. For the equals sign, children can discuss how the groups of things on both sides of the equals sign have the same amount, so the = symbol has two little marks that are the same length.

The second major extension in kindergarten is that children can use larger numbers. They solve problems with totals up through 10 as word problems and as equations.

Fingers

Prekindergarten and kindergarten children become able to use their fingers to add or to subtract for totals ≤10. When counting all, they will—

- count out and raise fingers for the first addend,
- count out and raise fingers for the second addend, and
- then count all the raised fingers.

Some children learn at home or in a care center to put the addends on separate hands, whereas others continue on to the next fingers for the second addend. Using separate hands makes it easier to see the addends. Continuing on the same hand makes it easier to see the total. Both methods can be modeled by the teacher. As children become more and more familiar with which group of fingers makes four or five or seven fingers, they may not even have to count out the total because they can feel or see the total fingers. Similarly, children using the method of putting addends on separate hands eventually can just raise the fingers for the addends without counting out each addend by ones. But they do need initially to count the total. Children who put addends on separate hands may have difficulty with problems with addends over 5 (e.g., 6 + 3) because one cannot put both numbers on separate hands. They can, however, continue raising fingers. Because these problems involve adding 1 or 2, such continuations of 1 and 2 are relatively easy.

When subtracting on their fingers, children raise fingers to show the total and then bend down or separate the fingers that show the number taken away (the known addend). They then can see or count the remaining fingers to find what is left (the unknown addend).

Some people worry that children who use their fingers will end up using them "as a crutch" and will not advance. But the research-based learning path of methods discussed later demonstrates that fingers are used in different ways. At level 1 they are used as the objects that present the situation and that are added or taken away. But at level 2, it is the number words themselves that have become the objects that present the situation and that are added or taken away. The fingers count or match the second addend when counting on. These level 2 methods are advanced enough to be used for life. So fingers are a useful learning tool, and they are used worldwide. What is important is that children in grade 1 advance to using fingers in level 2 counting on and not remain at level 1 methods (this is discussed later).

Language learning

Addition and subtraction situations, and the word problems that describe such situations, provide many wonderful opportunities for learning language. Word problems are short and fairly predictable texts. Children can vary words in them while keeping much of the text. Children can say word problems in their own words and help everyone's understanding. English language learners can repeat such texts and vary particular words as they wish. All these learning activities require the support of visual objects or acted-out situations for children to learn the special mathematics vocabulary involved in addition and subtraction. These additive and subtractive learning situations provide wonderful opportunities for children to integrate art (drawing pictures), language practice, and pretend play.

Through experiences of relating actions and words in a story situation, children gradually extend their vocabulary of words that mean to add: *in all, put together, total, and, together,* and *altogether* (the most difficult term for children). They also learn words that mean to subtract: *are left, the rest,* and *take away.* Children can begin posing such word problems as well as solving them. Most will initially need help with asking the questions, the most difficult aspect of posing word problems. As with all language learning, it is very important for children to talk and to use the language themselves. Having children retell a word problem in their own words is a powerful general teaching strategy for helping students talk in mathematical sentences. Such retelling is especially important for English language learners to extend children's knowledge and give them practice speaking in English.

It is very important that kindergarten teachers *do not* teach "key word" strategies, where a single word in the problem tells you what operation to do. Of course, children must learn the meaning of the mathematical language, but the emphasis should always be on understanding the situation, not just one word. So later on in kindergarten, the teacher should give problems in which key words would lead to the wrong solution so that children learn to listen to the whole problem. *Eat* often means take away the things that are eaten, so children could be asked an addition problem like *Bryan ate three crackers. Karen ate two crackers. How many crackers did they eat?* This continues to be important to do in later grades to encourage children to listen to or read the whole text.

Partners as embedded numbers

With experience in the foregoing addition/subtraction situations, children begin to learn to see partners (addends) hiding inside a number. For example, children can take apart 5 to see that it can be made from a 3 and a 2. Later on, they can systematically take apart five things to see all its partners: three and two and also four and one. In kindergarten, these decomposed/composed numbers can be symbolized by equations such as $5 = 3 + 2$ and $5 = 4 + 1$. Such equations give children experiences with the meaning of the = symbol as *is the same number as* and with algebraic equations with one number on the left. This is helpful in later algebra learning because many algebra students think that equations must produce an answer and that only one number can be alone on the right side of the equation.

Kindergartners can work on partners of numbers through 10. After work using objects to find partners, they also show partners in drawings and/or on activity sheets. Such work is also recorded with numbers in expressions and equations as they complete equations to show number partners: $5 = \_\_\_ + \_\_\_$, and so on. Figures 2.5 and 2.6 describe and show examples of partner activities in kindergarten.

Step 1: Small totals ≤5

- See two small numbers (partners) hiding inside a total. Partners may be different colors or objects or grouped spatially. *I see one red and two blue blocks. Three has one and two hiding inside.*

- Tell partner stories for familiar situations. *My family has six people. Three are grown-ups and three are children.*

- Children also show partners on their fingers.

Step 2: Objects recorded with drawings for totals ≤10, especially with totals of 2 to 6 and 10

- With objects that show a given number, separate the objects into two partners using a break-apart stick or by separating spatially. Record the total above and the partners (connected by a + sign) below using number cards and a +/− card. Teacher makes math drawings and writes the numbers (as shown below).

- Do this repeatedly for different partners. The teacher records using math drawings and an expression, and later an equation, below. Children discuss the patterns they see.

6

| o│o o o o o | o o│o o o o | o o o│o o o |
| 1 + 5 | 2 + 4 | 3 + 3 |

| o o o o o│o | o o o o│o o | o o o│o o o |
| 5 + 1 | 4 + 2 | 3 + 3 |

Step 3: Drawings for totals ≤10, especially with totals of 2 to 6 and 10

- Children move to using activity sheets that show partners and totals (see figure 2.6). They move from filling partners into an expression (in part A) to filling partners into an equation (in part B) to writing the whole expression (in part C).

Different visual layouts recorded by the teacher and used on activity sheets help students see and discuss different patterns. The top layout in figure 2.6 shows the break-apart stick moving systematically to the right to make different partners. The bottom left vertical lay-out allows children to focus on the numerical pattern of the first partner getting smaller and the second partner getting bigger.

Step 4: Unknown partner games

- A pair of children can practice the partners in a number by laying out objects for a number and showing that number with a number card. While one child looks away, the other child separates the objects into partners and takes the objects for one partner. The first child then looks at the remaining partner and the total card and tells the unknown (missing) partner by visualizing, using fingers, or counting out objects for the total to see how many are gone. Number cards and a +/− card can then be used to label the partners. Or children can make a math drawing, cover one partner, and then write the partner expression or equation.

Fig. 2.5. Progression to show partners and totals

A. Write the partners. [Just write the partner numbers.]

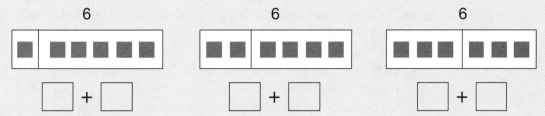

B. Write the partners. [Write the partner numbers in an equation.]

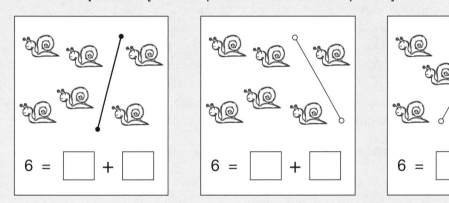

C. Write the partner equation. [Write a partner expression in an equation.]

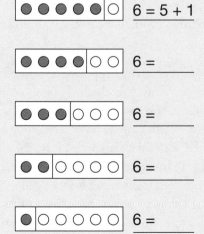

6 = 5 + 1

6 = _____

6 = _____

6 = _____

6 = _____

D. Same as B or C, but the children draw a line in each picture and finish the equation by writing partners for the B version and writing an expression for the C version.

Fig. 2.6. Seeing and writing partners

Roles of worksheets in kindergarten

The number, relations, and operations goals require kindergarten children to coordinate language, written mathematics symbols, and quantities shown in objects or drawings (and increasingly, mentally). Although kindergarten children need to act on objects initially, this becomes increasingly messy and complex with larger numbers and more complex ideas. We have seen how the learning progressions for tens in teens, for story problem solving related to equations, and work with partners of a number move from use of objects to use of drawings that children make themselves and of drawings of quantities and symbols with which children interact. It is important for children to have these experiences with conceptual-visual-symbolic worksheets. Because the term *worksheets* so often has rote connotations, especially for younger children, it might be better to call such conceptual-visual-symbolic pages *meaning-making and discussion* pages. This is a reminder that work with any such pages needs to reflect the central parts of table 1.1 in the introduction about effective teaching-learning practices. These pages that connect mathematical language and symbols to quantities and to actions in the world are used by the teacher to lead children's attention across these crucial aspects to help them see patterns and make connections within a nurturing and helping math-talk community. Students explain and help one another when they are practicing and engaging in meaning making with written mathematical symbols, and they reflect on and talk about their mathematical thinking.

The operations core developed in grade 1

Levels in addition/subtraction solution methods

A large body of research evidence describes the worldwide learning path of levels in addition and subtraction methods. These levels are shown in table 2.3. Children before and in kindergarten are working at level 1. As described above, they use count-all strategies to solve addition problems and take-away strategies to solve subtraction problems. The conceptual embedded numbers described above allow some kindergarten and all grade 1 children to move to a more advanced level of addition/subtraction solution procedures, level 2 counting on.

Level 2 counting on

First graders build on their earlier number and relations/operation knowledge and skills to advance to level 2 counting-on solution methods. They also come to understand that addition is related to subtraction and can think of subtraction as finding an unknown addend. Some children will have discovered counting on in kindergarten. They can share this method with their classmates. It is important to help all first graders move from counting all to counting on because they need this method to add and subtract numbers with teen totals and it is faster and more accurate even with smaller totals. Learning counting on can start with totals ≤10.

Counting on is not a rote method. For example, counting on for 8 + 6 requires a shift in word meaning for the first addend 8 from its *cardinal* meaning as eight things (to which six things are added) to a *counting* meaning as children count on six more from eight. Children then must shift from that last counted word to its cardinal meaning of how many objects there are in total. Children

Table 2.3
Levels of Children's Addition and Subtraction Methods

	8 + 6 = 14	14 − 8 = 6
Level 1: **Count all**	a 1 2 3 4 5 6 7 8 ○○○○○○○○ 1 2 3 4 5 6 7 8 c b 1 2 3 4 5 6 ○○○○○○ 9 10 11 12 13 14 1 2 3 4 5 6 9 10 11 12 13 14	a 1 2 3 4 5 6 7 8 9 10 11 12 13 14 ○○○○○○○○○○○○○○ 1 2 3 4 5 6 7 8 1 2 3 4 5 6 b c To solve 14 − 8: I count on 8 + ? = 14. 10 11 12 13 14 9 I took away 8. 8 to 14 is 6, so 14 − 8 = 6.
Level 2: **Count on**	8 ○○○○○○○○ ○○○○○○ 9 10 11 12 13 14 Or use fingers to keep track of the six counted on.	
Level 3: **Recompose** Make a 10 (general): One addend breaks apart to make 10 with the other addend.	10 + 4 ○○○○○○○○○○ ○○○○ ○○○○○ ○○○ ○○○○ ○ 10 2 4 +	14 − 8: I make a ten for 8 + ? = 14. ○○○○○○○○ ○○○ ○ 8 + 2 + 4 6 8 + 6 = 14
	Make a 10 (from 5s within each addend).	
Doubles ± n	6 + 8 = 6 + 6 + 2 = 12 + 2 = 14	

Note: Many children attempt to count down for subtraction, but counting down is difficult and error-prone. Children are much more successful with counting on; it makes subtraction as easy as addition.

can be helped to see these relationships by solving within some kind of structured visual setting. For example (see figure 2.7), seeing circles for both addends in a row with the problem printed above enables children to count both addends and then count all to find the total (their usual level 1 direct modeling solution method). But after counting all, they can be asked what number they say when they count the last circle in the group of six and whether they need to count all the objects or just start at six. Going back and forth between this counting on and the usual counting all enables children to see that counting on is just an abbreviation of counting all where the initial counts of the first addend are omitted. Trying this with different problems in the same layout enables many children to see this general pattern and begin counting on.

Transition strategies such as counting 1, 2, 3, 4, 5, 6 very quickly or very softly or saying the 6 (*siiiiiiixxxxxx*) slowly have been observed in students who are learning counting on by themselves; these can be suggested to facilitate this transition to counting on. Some weaker students may need explicit encouragement to *trust the 6* and omit the initial counting of the first addend, and they may need to use these transitional methods for a while to overcome the need to count all.

After such an initial introduction, children can devise and share their own ways of thinking about counting on. They can draw a circle around a math drawing of the first addend and write the numeral (e.g., 6) on top of the group. Soon they can just draw the circle with a 6 inside it. They can imagine the first addend as objects in front of them and gather them and hold them in one hand while saying *six* and start the count of the second addend (*seven, eight,* etc.), keeping track of this count with fingers of the other hand. This helps show the conceptual distinction between the two addends and enables children to remember that they start keeping track with the second addend (for example, 7), not with the first word said as the final count of the first addend (for example, 6).

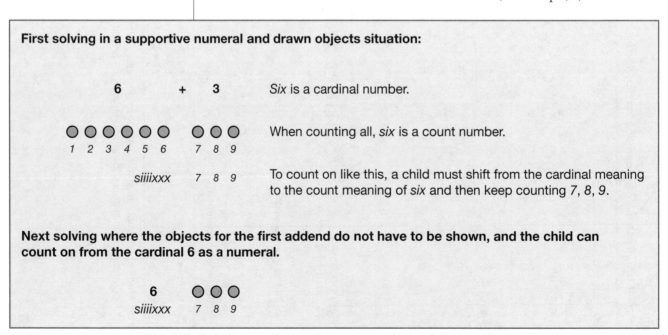

Fig. 2.7. Relating cardinal and count meanings when counting on

Keeping track of the second addend

Counting on requires keeping track of the second addend—of how many you count on so that you count on from the first addend exactly the number of the second addend. When the number is small, such as for 6 + 3, most children use perceptual subitizing (just seeing or feeling the small number) to keep track of the 3 counted on. This keeping track might involve actual objects, fingers, or drawn circles. But it can also use a mental visual image (some children say they see three things in their head and count them). Some children use auditory subitizing (they say they hear *7, 8, 9* as three words). For larger second addends, children use objects, fingers, or conceptual subitizing to keep track as they count on. For 8 + 6, they might think of 6 as 3 and 3 and count with groups of three: *8, ..., 9, 10, 11, ..., 12, 13, 14*, with a pause after the *9, 10, 11* to mark the first three words counted on. Other children might use a visual pattern (*I saw three circles and another three circles*) or an auditory rhythm to keep track of how many words they counted on. So here we see how the *perceptual subitizing* and the *conceptual subitizing* that begin very early come to be used in a more complex and advanced mathematical process. This is how numerical ideas build within a learning path, integrating earlier simple ideas into more complex processes or ideas. Children can discuss various methods of keeping track, and they can be helped to use one that will work for them. Almost all children can learn to use fingers successfully to keep track of the second addend. This is a useful rapid method because fingers are always available.

Counting on from the larger number

It is helpful initially in counting on to give problems where the first addend is the larger number. Later, when children understand counting on, they can discuss problems where the larger number is second. It is helpful if these problems are given in put-together situations where the order of the addends does not matter as much as it does in change situations. It is also helpful if one addend is large and the other quite small because when the addends are fairly close in size, some children prefer to count on starting with the first addend mentioned in the situation because they are more comfortable doing that. Children can discuss and justify why it is OK to start counting on from either addend (because you can count two groups in either order and you get the same total; they are the same objects).

Subtraction as an unknown addend: Counting on for subtraction

Many experiences with composing/decomposing (finding partners hiding inside a number) can give children the understanding that a total is any number that has partners (addends) that compose it. When subtracting by taking away, they have been seeing that they take away one of those addends, leaving the other one. These two kinds of experiences can combine into the understanding that subtracting means finding the unknown addend. Therefore, children can always solve subtraction problems by a forward method that finds the unknown addend, thus avoiding the difficult and error-prone counting down methods that so many children in the United States invent and use. Children in many other countries are helped to use the more accurate forward methods. It is equally appropriate to do so in this country. The forward level 2 counting-on and level 3 recomposing methods for subtracting are shown in table 2.3. These methods will be invented by some first graders, especially for unknown-addend problem types to be discussed in the next section. These inventions can be shared with classmates.

But all children can benefit from discussing and then practicing counting on for subtraction in supportive visual situations. Table 2.3 shows in level 2 one such visual situation. Taking away needs to be linked to a count-on object situation initially. In the left drawing in table 2.3, the first eight objects can be taken away, saying, "I take away eight. Then I count on using some method to keep track of how many are left." Or in a math drawing, a line can be drawn through the objects in the first addend. It is important to take away or draw a line through the *first* objects because taking away the last objects suggests counting down. The right side of level 2 in table 2.3 shows counting on without objects and using fingers to keep track. Children can use their usual keeping-track method to subtract as well as to add when counting on. Keeping track is actually easier for subtracting than for adding because you do not need to monitor the fingers or visual or auditory pattern as you go. You are going to stop when you hear the total. Then you look at your fingers, or consider the visual or auditory pattern, to find out how many are in the second addend. When someone is counting on, you cannot tell from watching whether he or she is adding or subtracting. These look and sound the same; only the function of the keeping-track method varies. Children should discuss and see explicitly how a subtraction situation such as $9 - 6 = ?$ is solved by finding the unknown addend in the situation $6 + ? = 9$. Learning to subtract by counting on allows children to solve a wider range of word problems (discussed in a later section).

Level 3 recomposing methods including the general make-a-ten methods

Many first graders will also move on to the level 3 recomposing solution methods (see table 2.3). The doubles plus or minus one (or even two) are commonly used by many children in the United States, but they are not general and cannot be used for many problems with teen totals ($9 + 2, 9 + 3, 9 + 4, 9 + 5, 9 + 6, 8 + 3, 8 + 4, 8 + 5,$ and $7 + 4$). The general make-a-ten methods do work for all teen totals. They are taught in East Asia and in many other countries. These make-a-ten methods change a problem like $8 + 6$ into the equivalent problem $10 + 4$. This involves three steps (see the drawing in table 2.3). Each step is a prerequisite for the make-a-ten methods:

- Step 1 is to make a ten with the first (or the larger) addend by breaking the second addend into the part that will make ten and the rest; $8 + 6 = 8 + 2$ (to make ten) $+ ?$. Therefore, the first prerequisite is for children to know all the partners of 10.
- Step 2 is to find the partner in the second addend: $6 = 2 + ?$. The second prerequisite is knowing all the partners of numbers from 2 to 9.
- Step 3 is to add 10 and the partner found in the previous step: $10 + 4$. The third prerequisite is seeing the tens in teen numbers ($10 + 4 = 14$), which was discussed in the number core.

Children in many East Asian countries develop these prerequisites before first grade. They are consolidated in early first grade and then used in the grade 1 units that teach making a ten for addition and for subtraction. A similar approach could be used in the United States if children were supported to develop the prerequisites in kindergarten or in grade 1. This method is more difficult in English than in East Asian languages where the teen numbers are said with a ten (e.g., 14 is ten four, so the last step is particularly easy). In the United States, many first graders can learn the make-a-ten methods for addition and subtraction, but others learn it in second grade when doing multidigit addition or subtraction (see *Focus in Grade 2* [NCTM, forthcoming]). Many children remain more comfortable with counting on, and this method can be fast and accurate enough for teen totals to remain the main method for them.

The importance of work with partners (addends)

Two of the foregoing three prerequisites for the make-a-ten methods involve understanding and fluency with partners of numbers ≤ 10. Kindergartners can begin this partner work by finding partners and writing expressions for them and eventually finding all of the partners for a given number systematically. Figure 2.8 shows an activity sheet (on the left) to follow up after partner work with objects in kindergarten or grade 1. This sheet organizes the partners so

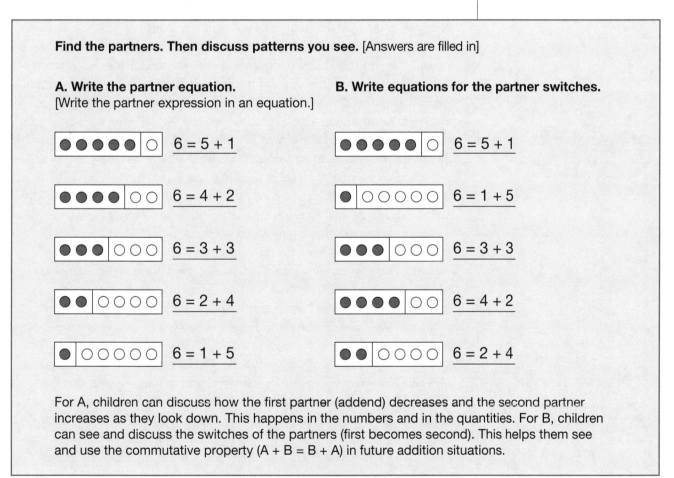

Find the partners. Then discuss patterns you see. [Answers are filled in]

A. Write the partner equation.
[Write the partner expression in an equation.]

6 = 5 + 1

6 = 4 + 2

6 = 3 + 3

6 = 2 + 4

6 = 1 + 5

B. Write equations for the partner switches.

6 = 5 + 1

6 = 1 + 5

6 = 3 + 3

6 = 4 + 2

6 = 2 + 4

For A, children can discuss how the first partner (addend) decreases and the second partner increases as they look down. This happens in the numbers and in the quantities. For B, children can see and discuss the switches of the partners (first becomes second). This helps them see and use the commutative property (A + B = B + A) in future addition situations.

Fig. 2.8. Seeing patterns for partners

that children can discuss the compensating patterns as one partner increases and the other decreases. Children love to see and discuss this pattern for all numbers ≤ 10. Grade 1 children can move on to the pattern shown on the right in figure 2.8. Here the partners of a number are organized into their *partner switches,* where the order of the partners (addends) is switched. First graders can discuss these patterns and why they work (they are the same objects, just switched in order: it does not matter what order you count them in). Seeing the commutative principle in action for all numbers is helpful for basic additions and subtractions. Working with partners of numbers helps children see a total as made of up various pairs of numbers. These relationships help children construct the level 2 embedded number conceptions of solution methods and of word problems, the prerequisites for the level 3 make-a-ten methods, and fluency with small additions and subtractions.

More difficult problem types in grade 1: Solving algebraic problems

Learning to mathematize and model addition and subtraction situations with objects, fingers, and drawings is the foundation for algebraic problem solving. More difficult types of the problem situations already discussed (change and collection situations) can be given from grade 1 on. Children can also solve these problems by modeling the situation, but the model does not produce the answer as do the simpler problems discussed earlier. Instead, the solver needs to reflect on the model to find the solution to the problem. This is exactly what happens in algebra. You represent a problem situation by an equation (a model of the situation), and then you solve the equation using the methods of algebra. Therefore, we can think of the more difficult problems (where modeling the situation does not automatically produce the answer) as algebraic problems. Young children develop their own conceptual ways to find the solution by using their situation representations. These representations can be with objects, drawn models, or equations. Children's solutions of these algebraic problems depend on their level of thinking as reflected in the levels of solution methods in table 2.3. These levels are a learning path of increasingly abstract, embedded, and general methods of representing and solving problems.

Figure 2.9 shows all the types of the addition and subtraction real-world situations created by varying the unknown in each type discussed above and including the new grade 1 additive comparison type. Each problem situation involves three quantities, so there are three different subtypes for each main type. First graders can and do solve these problem subtypes by modeling them with objects and fingers. But they can move on to using equations or numerical drawings to show each kind of situation. They have been representing the simpler problem situations with equations. The left-to-right format of equations parallels nicely the actions in change-plus and change-minus situations. Children easily learn to write the situation equations for the unknown-change and unknown-start problem subtypes (see figure 2.9): $9 + \square = 13$ ($9 +$ what $= 13$), $\square + 4 = 13$, $13 - \square = 4$, $\square - 9 = 4$. These *situation equations* show the situation; they are not *solution equations* that show what to do with the numbers to get the answer. Thus, algebraic problems are those in which the situation equation for the problem (the equation that represents the situation) is not the solution equation. Rather, the solver has to think about the situation equation to solve the problem represented by the situation equation. The research literature shows that children often invent such situation equation forms before they see them used by other children or by teachers or books. They are natural forms of modeling for children.

The collection situations involve a total that is decomposed into two partners (addends). The total or an addend can be the unknown. Some textbooks in this country model such problems by a part-part-total model of a rectangle with a segment across it and then the bottom half separated into two parts. But this model is confusing to some children because it involves double objects: those making the total and those making the parts. And the parts look equal, which they usually are not. The Math Mountain discussed in *Focus in Kindergarten* (NCTM 2010) and shown for the collection situations in figure 2.9 shows both the total and the parts, but the inverted V form clarifies that they move together or apart to change into each other.

Types of Addition and Subtraction Situations, Part I

Change Situations

Change Plus		*Change Minus*	
Unknown Result	$9 + 4 = \square$	**Unknown Result**	$13 - 9 = \square$
Dan had 9 cherries. Then he picked 4 more. How many does he have now?		Dan had 13 cherries. Then he ate 9 of them. How many does he have now?	
Unknown Change	$9 + \square = 13$	**Unknown Change**	$13 - \square = 4$
Dan had 9 cherries. Then he picked some more. Now he has 13 cherries. How many did he pick?		Dan had 13 cherries. Then he ate some of them. Now he has 4 cherries. How many did he eat?	
Unknown Start	$\square + 4 = 13$	**Unknown Start**	$\square - 9 = 4$
Dan had some cherries. Then he picked 4 more. Now he has 13 cherries. How many did he start with?		Dan had some cherries. Then he ate 9 of them. Now he has 4 cherries. How many did he start with?	

Collection Situations

Unknown Total	*Unknown Partner*
Put Together 9 4	**Put Together** 13 / 9 $\square$
Ana put 9 dimes and 4 nickels in her pocket. How many coins did she put in her pocket?	Ana put 13 coins in her pocket. 9 are dimes and the rest are nickels. How many nickels are in her pocket?
Take Apart	**Take Apart**
Ana put 9 coins in her purse and 4 coins in her bank. How many coins did she have in the beginning?	Ana had 13 coins. She put 9 in her purse and the rest in her bank. How many coins did she put in her bank?
No Action	**No Action**
Ana has 9 dimes and 4 nickels. How many coins does she have in all?	Ana has 13 coins. 9 are dimes and the rest are nickels. How many are nickels? *Either partner can be unknown.*

Fig. 2.9. Types of addition and subtraction situations (part I) (*Continued on next page*)

Types of Addition and Subtraction Situations, Part II

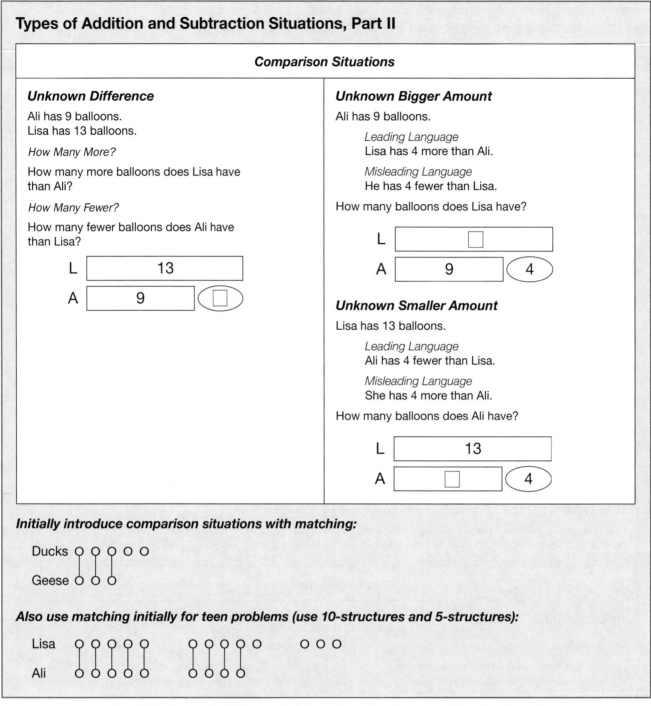

Comparison Situations

Unknown Difference

Ali has 9 balloons.
Lisa has 13 balloons.

How Many More?

How many more balloons does Lisa have than Ali?

How Many Fewer?

How many fewer balloons does Ali have than Lisa?

Unknown Bigger Amount

Ali has 9 balloons.

Leading Language
Lisa has 4 more than Ali.

Misleading Language
He has 4 fewer than Lisa.

How many balloons does Lisa have?

Unknown Smaller Amount

Lisa has 13 balloons.

Leading Language
Ali has 4 fewer than Lisa.

Misleading Language
She has 4 more than Ali.

How many balloons does Ali have?

Initially introduce comparison situations with matching:

Ducks

Geese

Also use matching initially for teen problems (use 10-structures and 5-structures):

Lisa

Ali

Fig. 2.9. Types of addition and subtraction situations (part II)—*Continued*

Solving these algebraic problems requires emphasizing the most crucial problem-solving strategy—understand the situation and make a drawing if it will help you. Key-word strategies in which children focus only on one or a few words will not work with algebraic problems. Teachers need to help all children move beyond such limiting strategies by emphasizing understanding the situation.

Additive comparison situations

Additive comparison situations compare a large quantity to a smaller quantity *to find the difference.* These are complex situations that are usually not solvable until grade 1. The third quantity, the *difference,* is not physically present in the situation. Children must come to see the differences as the *extra leftovers* in the bigger quantity or the *amount the smaller quantity needs to gain* to be the same as the bigger quantity. As discussed earlier, the language involved in additive comparison situations is challenging because English gives two kinds of information in the same sentence: *Emily has five more than Tommy* says both that *Emily has more than Tommy* and that *she has five more.* Many children do not initially hear the *five.* They will need help and practice identifying and using the two kinds of information in this kind of sentence by saying it in two parts. If children have not had earlier experiences with comparing situations before grade 1, they may need to stay with math drawings that show all the objects and match or count the objects as shown at the bottom of figure 2.9 rather than use the numerical comparison bars shown by the problems. Simple picture graphs that show a picture for each object can be used to ask comparison questions. Two rows and two columns of pictures are appropriate for grade 1, where children are still trying to sort out the language. Children can also ask questions about such graphs that are other situation types, such as *How many balls in all?* for a graph with two rows of balls.

After children can make a math drawing whose objects they can match, they can begin to write an equation to go with their math drawing. Research indicates that different children choose different equation forms for the same problem. For the unknown-difference problem shown in figure 2.9, children may write $9 + \square = 13$ or $13 - 9 = \square$. The subtraction equations might be solved by level 2 counting on from 9 to 13 rather than by taking away. Textbooks often consider comparison problems just to be subtraction problems and show only the subtraction equation $13 - 9 = \square$. But children think about these situations in different ways and should not be pushed toward only a subtraction representation.

Each comparison sentence or question can be said in two basic ways: Either of the compared quantities can be said first, and the comparison word can be *more* or *fewer.* Children should hear and say problems that use the word *fewer* or *less* and not just *more.* Practicing saying the comparison both ways is helpful in building the linguistic competence for these situations. First graders can also use *equalizing* forms of the comparing sentence or question that suggest actions (see the sidebar Examples of Equalizing Language).

These equalizing action forms often are easier for children even though the sentences are longer. A math drawing of a comparison situation will support children's saying of the comparison in different ways. It can also help them see that these sentences all are describing the same quantity: the *difference* between the smaller and the bigger quantity.

When one of the compared quantities is unknown (see the right column of part II figure 2.9), one form of the comparing statement is misleading because the word in the statement is the opposite of the solution action. For example, in the problem—

Examples of Equalizing Language

For example, the comparing form is

How many fewer balloons does Ali have than Lisa?

and its equalizing form is

How many balloons does Ali need to get to have as many as Lisa has?

This is an equalizing action form because it suggests making the number of balloons equal by **adding** some balloons to Ali's balloons so that his equal Lisa's.

The other comparing form is

How many more balloons does Lisa have than Ali?

and its equalizing form is

How many balloons does Lisa need to give away to have as many as Ali?

This is an equalizing action form because it suggests making the number of balloons equal by **subtracting** some balloons from Lisa's balloons so that hers equal Ali's.

> Ali has 9 balloons. He has 4 fewer balloons than Lisa has.
> How many balloons does Lisa have?

the comparing sentence (in italics) says *fewer*. But to find the number of balloons Lisa has, you need to *add* 4 to 9, not subtract 4 as the word *fewer* suggests. This is the misleading comparing sentence. The nonmisleading sentence is "Lisa has 4 more balloons than Ali has" because the word *more* suggests adding 4 to 9, which is the correct solution. The misleading language problems are too difficult for many first graders who may be struggling with the difficult English sentences; they can be postponed until grade 2.

Levels of thinking and the word-problem subtypes

Table 2.4 shows how the levels of thinking that support the levels of solution methods in table 2.3 are used in the change and collection addition/subtraction word-problem subtypes. The easy problems solvable before grade 1 by

Table 2.4
Levels in Addition/Subtraction Word Problems and in Solution Methods

Level	Word Problem Type	Numerical Solution Method
Level 1 Easy	Direct model with objects or math drawing	
	Change Plus: Unknown Result	ooooo ooooo ooo $9 + 4 = \square$
	Collection: Unknown Total	ooooo ooooo ooo $9 + 4 = \square$
	Change Minus: Unknown Result	~~ooooo ooooo~~ ooo $13 - 9 = \square$
Level 2 Medium	**Easy types, new Count On solution methods**	Embedded addend methods o o o o 9 10 11 12 13
	Change Plus: Unknown Result Collection: Unknown Total	Count On to Find the Total: stop when feel 4 fingers, hear 13; answer is 13 Count On from First, then Count On from Larger
	Change Minus: Unknown Result	Count On to Find an Addend: stop when hear 13 see 4 fingers; answer is 4 (do this after the next two types)
	Medium types	
	Change Plus: Unknown Change Collection: Unknown Addend	Count On to Find an Addend [Do these before solving $13 - 9$ as $9 + \square = 13$]
	Change Minus: Unknown Change	Switch addends: $13 - \square = 9$ becomes $13 - 9 = \square$ [count on from 9 to 13]
Level 3 Difficult	Change Plus: Unknown Start	Commutativity: $\square + 4 = 13$ becomes $4 + \square = 13$
	Change Minus: Unknown Start	Reversibility: $\square - 9 = 4$ becomes $4 + 9 = \square$
	All earlier types may be solved by the new Level 3 Derived Facts solution methods	Derived Facts (chunks within addends) Make a Ten: $9 + 4 = 9 + 1 + 3 = 10 + 3 = 13$ $9 + \square = 13$, so $9 + 1 + 3$ and $1 + 3$ is 4, so 4

level 1 methods of counting all and taking away are shown at the top along with object solution methods, equations, and Math Mountain drawings. Level 2 shows how the level 1 easy subtypes come to be solved by the level 2 counting on methods, as discussed above. Three subtypes of medium difficulty become solvable at this level. They all involve an unknown addend: collection unknown addend, change plus unknown change, and change minus unknown change. The all can be solved by counting on to find the unknown addend.

Many first graders can solve the level 3 difficult problems, the change-plus and change-minus unknown start problems. Class discussions in which children show their representation of the situation and share their solution thinking can help more children solve these problems. The change-plus problem requires children to use commutativity of the addends so they can start counting on or making a ten from the known addend. Either the equation or the Math Mountain facilitates this understanding. The change-minus problem is solved by mentally reversing the situation to add the two known addends. Children who are at level 3 may solve any problem by the level 3 recomposing methods or by just knowing the addition or unknown addend answer.

Comparison problems may continue to be solved by making math drawings of the situation and then matching or counting. Some children may move on to writing an equation, as discussed above. Especially for comparison with larger numbers such as teen totals, many children can benefit from seeing the comparison bars shown in part II of figure 2.9 and writing the numbers in these bars and labeling the bars to show who/which is *more/less*. Children who still want to make math drawings of objects should be allowed to do so, but they can be encouraged to show the problem in another way also (comparison bars or an equation, or some children even use the Math Mountain shown in figure 2.9 for comparing situations). Having children discuss these multiple ways of showing and solving comparison situations provides needed experience in thinking about and saying comparison language.

Number lines are not appropriate for children before grade 2

A great deal of confusion arises about what the term *number line* means. Two NRC reports (Kilpatrick, Swafford, and Findell 2001; Cross, Woods, and Schweingruber 2009) recommend that number lines not be used until grade 2 because they are conceptually too difficult for younger children. In early childhood materials including kindergarten, the term *number line* or *mental number line* often really means a *number path*, such as in the common early childhood games where numbers are put on squares and children move along such a numbered path. Such number paths are count models in which things are counted. Each square is a thing that can be counted, so these are appropriate for children from age two through grade 1. A number path and a number line are shown in figure 2.10 along with the meanings that children must understand and relate when using these models. A number line is a length model such as a ruler or a bar graph in which numbers are represented by the length from zero along a line segmented into equal lengths. Children need to count the length units on a number line, not the numbers. Young children have difficulties with such a number-line representation because they have difficulty seeing the units—they need to see things, so they focus on the numbers or the segmenting marks instead of on the lengths. Thus they may count the starting point 0 and then be off by one, or they may focus on the spaces and be confused by the location of the numbers at the ends of the spaces.

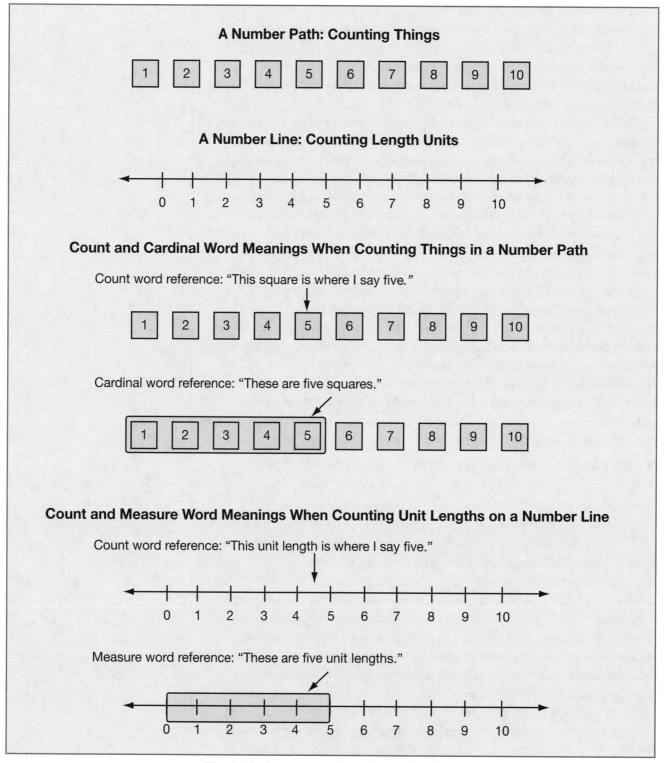

Fig. 2.10. A number path and a number line

It is important to show in classrooms for young children a *number list* (a list of numbers in order) or a *number path* (a list of numbers inside identical objects, such as the squares in figure 2.10), or the numbers can be beside the objects. Groupings that show these numbers can also be shown (e.g., the 5-groups can be above or beside the numbers 6 through 10). Children can play games and count along such number paths or number lists.

Table 2.3, addition/subtraction solution methods, shows how children will come to use the number-word list (the number-word sequence) as a *mental tool* for solving addition and subtraction problems with totals up to 18. They are able in grades 1 and 2 to use increasingly abbreviated and abstract solution methods, such as the counting-on and the make-a-ten methods. At this point the number words themselves have become unitized mental objects to be added, subtracted, and ordered. The original separate sequence, counting, and cardinal meanings have become related and finally integrated over several years into a *truly numerical mental number-word sequence.* These most advanced methods depend on the whole teaching-learning path discussed in the foregoing. Many researchers have noted how the number-word list turns into a mental representational tool for adding and subtracting. A few researchers have called this a *mental number line.* However, this mental representation cannot be a mental number line for young children, because children in kindergarten and grade 1 are using a *mental number-word list* (sequence) as a count model—each number word is taken as a unit to be counted, matched, added, or subtracted.

The use of number lines such as in a ruler or a bar-graph scale is an important part of measurement and is discussed in that section. In grade 2, these related representations all form an appropriate important part of the learning goals. But they are too complex for many children at earlier ages. The distinction between a number path/list and a number line continues into models for presenting data. A *picture graph* is a *number path* in which identical pictures (things) are used to show how many in all. In the simple graphs used in grade 1, one picture stands for one thing. Usually no numbers are present; one just counts the pictures. If numbers are shown on such a graph, they are placed in the middle of each picture, counting and summing the pictures, as in a number path. A *bar graph* uses a *number line* (bar-graph scale) to show the length of the bars in the graph.

Multidigit addition and subtraction

Thinking about adding tens and ones within two-digit numbers can increase children's understanding of these units and of place value. Seeing the patterns involved in adding different place values is an important part of initial place-value work and could be considered part of the two-digit number core rather than as part of the operations core. Three kinds of patterns can be considered initially—

- adding some ones to some tens (e.g., 20 + 7 or 6 + 30),
- adding some ones to some ones (e.g., 2 + 7 or 6 + 3), and
- adding some tens to some tens (e.g., 20 + 70 or 60 + 30).

Doing such problems helps children learn to look at the position of the digit to decide what to add to what. Secret-code cards and math drawings of tens and ones can help children make sense of these problems and add the like units. This understanding of adding like units is crucial in general multidigit addition. These three patterns can also be examined for subtraction (e.g., $90 - 7$, $9 - 7$, $90 - 70$).

Other kinds of early place-value activities can help children see and work with the tens and ones values. Children can play a game in which they start with a number and then randomly draw cards that say 10 or 1 to see which to add on. This can help them focus on the tens or ones places and see which value to increase (e.g., 26 plus 10 is 36, but 26 plus 1 is 27). Children can also do activities to help them differentiate teen and decade words that sound alike (e.g., 18 and 80). Children can make them with secret-code cards, show them with finger flashes (18 is ten fingers and then eight fingers, but 80 is eight flashes of ten fingers), and show them with math drawings.

Understanding the patterns in adding 2 two-digit numbers is a more advanced step than the foregoing simpler patterns. Traditionally, first-grade children in the United States are given only two-digit addition and subtraction problems that do not involve regrouping (trading, carrying/borrowing). Such problems have frequently appeared on standardized tests. When children see only this kind of problem, especially if given in a vertical format, they can be lured into seeing such problems as two vertical columns. Figure 2.11 shows how solving pages of such problems creates a visual set of looking only at the columns (see row B). As a consequence, some second graders cannot even read the 2 two-digit numbers in a two-digit addition or subtraction problem. They only see, and therefore can only say, four separate single-digit numbers. Even worse, this vertical visual frame, and the learned solution method of adding or subtracting each column, leads to the errors shown in row C of figure 2.11. Children do not know what to do when they add and get a total of ten or more, so they just write it below the ones column. In subtraction, they just subtract the two numbers they see even if the smaller number is on the top. This is an extremely frequent error in grade 2, with only about a third of second graders correctly solving such problems requiring regrouping, primarily because of this error. We set up children in this country to make such errors by giving in grade 1 only problems that will lead them to make such errors.

Whether children see two-digit addition problems written horizontally or vertically, they need to think of each number as composed of tens and ones. Asking children to make a math drawing for such a problem using ten-sticks and ones (see the top of figure 2.12) can help focus children on the two-digit numbers and on the number of tens and of ones in each number. If necessary, the teacher can draw a rectangle around each number to facilitate this view. Making each number with secret-code cards (see the middle of figure 2.12) also can help children see each number as a decade number and ones (e.g., fifty and eight) as well as some tens and some ones (e.g., 5 tens and 8 ones). Math drawings can be made at the board or on paper, so they are easier to show the whole class when discussing solution methods than are tens and ones manipulatives such as base-ten blocks or cubes organized in tens.

	Addition	Subtraction
A. Typical problems with no ungrouping given in U.S. grade 1 (problems with ungrouping typically are not given)	5 1 + 3 6	8 7 − 3 6
B. Because children learn to solve problems in A by adding or subtracting each column separately, they come to have this column view of the problems. They operate only on the columns and do not think of the whole 2-digit numbers or the values.	5 1 + 3 6	8 7 − 3 6
C. This leads them to make the following typical errors in grade 2 on problems with regrouping such as 58 + 36 or 94 − 36. Only about a third of grade 2 students subtract such problems correctly, primarily because of this error.	5 8 + 3 6 ——— 814	9 4 − 3 6 ——— 6 2
	Add, but not make a new ten	Subtract in each column even if the top number is smaller than the bottom number.

Fig. 2.11. Grade 2 errors produced by only giving problems without regrouping in Grade 1

Figure 2.12 shows at the bottom two other steps that can support children in seeing and thinking about two separate two-digit numbers initially.

- Problems initially can be given in word problem situations because children will see and read two separate two-digit numbers.
- Problems can be written horizontally (58 + 36) rather than vertically because the + sign separates the 2 two-digit numbers.

However, it is easier to add the like units (adding tens to tens and adding ones to ones) in problems written vertically, and this vertical format can also make regrouping easier. So children need to learn to write and use the vertical format meaningfully.

In a classroom environment where children know that they need to make sense of and explain their solution methods, children can invent methods for adding two-digit numbers with regrouping. Math drawings of tens and ones can serve as thinking tools in this process. But it is vital that children do not use math drawings (or manipulatives like base-ten blocks or cubes organized into tens and ones) in a rote manner just to get an answer. The explicit goal needs to be to develop a written method using numbers and to show the steps with numbers as well as with the quantities in the math drawings. The quantities of

In 2-digit addition, it is important for children to see and think about the 2-digit numbers as being tens and ones and not just as a total quantity of ones or as two single digits. This *tens-and-ones conception* can be supported by making math drawings that show the tens and the ones.

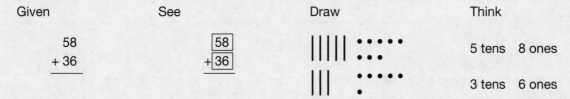

The *tens-and-ones conception* can also be supported by making the numbers with secret-code cards and then separating the tens and the ones.

Make fifty eight
and thirty six.

Take the ones off the tens.
See the tens and ones.

Think:

| 5 | 8 |
| 3 | 6 |

| 50 | 8 |
| 30 | 6 |

fifty and eight (or 5 tens 8 ones)

thirty and six (or 3 tens 6 ones)

It is also helpful in supporting the *tens-and-ones conception* to:

- Start 2-digit adding with word problems because children must read the 2-digit numbers within the problems.

- Write the problem horizontally to decrease the chance of children seeing the numbers using the vertical frame shown in figure 2.11 (just looking at the columns).

Problems written vertically as in the top example do make adding the like units (adding tens to tens and adding ones to ones) easier. It can also make regrouping easier. So children do need to be able to write and use the vertical format meaningfully.

Fig. 2.12. Seeing and reasoning with the 2-digit numbers within 2-digit addition

tens and ones need to be related to the written numerals in a solution method. Questions that can guide this process for children are these:

- Will you get a new ten or not?
- Where will you write your new ten in your number problem?

The kinds of methods children do invent and share are shown in figures 2.13, 2.14, and 2.15. The methods in figures 2.13 and 2.14 involve adding the ones and recording that total and adding the tens and recording that total. These four methods are all variations of a standard algorithmic approach that works for numbers of any size or any kind: add like quantities, and, if necessary, give ten of one unit as one of the next-left unit (called *regrouping, grouping, trading,* or *carrying*).

Figure 2.13 shows two general and accessible methods for adding two-digit numbers. Also shown are math drawings using tens and ones and explanations children might give for each step in their method. It is important for children to explain their methods using language that refers to the tens and ones quantities. The language for the tens might use decade words

(I added fifty and thirty to get eighty), or it might use tens words (I added 5 tens and 3 tens to get 8 tens). But children should not just say, "I added five and three" when they are adding tens. Children need to relate steps in their drawing to steps in their written method. Initially children will begin with a step in the math drawing, but as the numerical method takes on more meaning, the numerical step will be first. Eventually children will not need the drawing, but the numerical method will retain the images and quantitative meanings of the drawing. For many children, this may not happen until grade 2. Children need to learn to stand beside their drawing so that classmates can see it and point to parts of their drawing or numerical method as they explain. This helps their classmates understand their thinking.

In the math drawings, children may show the 5-groups in various ways. In figure 2.13, the top child has drawn the 5-groups horizontally, and the bottom child has drawn them vertically. This has led to them making the new ten in different ways. The top child encircles two more from the 6 to make a 10 with the 8. This could help children see the level 3 make-a-ten method and use it as their mental method. The bottom child has made a 10 from the 5 in 8 and the 5 in 6. This also is a mental method that some children use. These drawings reflect differences in how children choose to show 5-groups and the addition of the ones. They are not related to the overall method for adding the two-digit numbers.

The method shown at the top of figure 2.13, the new-groups-below method, is like the common method where the new 1 ten is written above the tens place except that the new 1 ten is written below, waiting until the tens are added. This new-groups-below method has several advantages over the common method (which could be called the new-groups-above method and is shown in figure 2.14).

- You can clearly see the 14 ones in the first step, with the 1 ten in 14 put down below in the tens place waiting to be added.
- Children can write 14 in their normal order: write 1 then 4. With new groups above, children are encouraged to write the 4 ones and then carry the 1 to the tens column. Sometimes children reverse this, and it may just be that they are writing 14 in their usual order rather than making a conceptual error.
- With the new ten below, you can add the two numbers of tens you see (5 tens and 3 tens to get 8 tens) and then add the new 1 ten waiting below. With new groups above, children either often add the two numbers they see (5 and 3) and then forget to add the 1 new ten above, or they are encouraged to add the 1 new ten to the top number and then hold that number (6 tens) in their head, ignore the top number they can see (the 5 tens), and add the number in their head to the 3 tens. This is difficult.
- Some children object to the new-groups-above method, saying, "You're changing the problem." And this method does change the original problem 58 + 36 by adding the new 1 ten into the top number. In new groups below, the new 1 ten waits below in the space for

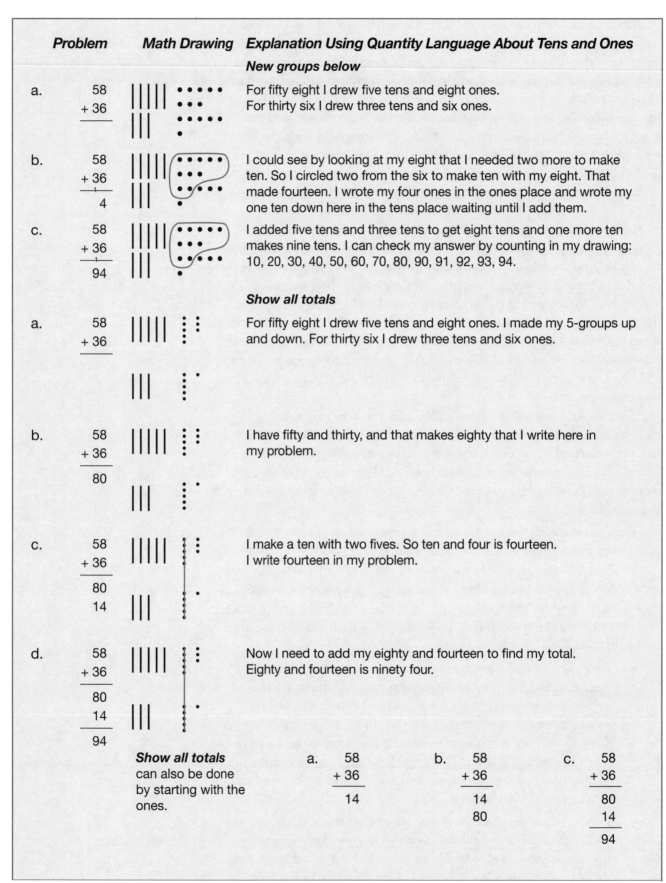

Fig. 2.13. General and accessible methods for adding 2-digit numbers

the total and gets added in to make the correct total. So visually this method also supports children seeing three horizontal multidigit numbers: the two addends and below that, the total.

The new-groups-below method is as general as the new-groups-above method, and it relates easily to the method many parents know. But for all of the foregoing reasons, it is more accessible to children and can reduce common errors.

Children using the show-all-totals method shown in the bottom half of figure 2.13 can add the tens first (can go left to right), which many children prefer. Children can also add the ones first (go right to left), as shown at the very bottom. This method is an expanded-notation method that allows children to see the total of the tens as a decade number 80. The secret-code cards shown in figure 2.12 help children with this method because the cards remind children that 58 is 50 and 8. The math drawing reminds them that 58 is 5 tens and 8 ones. This show-all-totals method can be done in later grades even with numbers of six or eight digits, but by then students who prefer this method often do not need the support of seeing the values of each place written out and can shorten to one of the other methods.

Figure 2.14 shows two other general methods. These methods are more difficult than the accessible methods shown in figure 2.13. The common new-groups-above method that was contrasted with the easier new-groups-below method is the method many parents in this country learned. Therefore, it is likely to be taught to some children at home and be brought into the classroom. Children who can understand and explain it of course can be allowed to use it. If no child introduces it to the classroom, this method still should be introduced as a method they may see other people use, so they should understand how it works. It is easy for children to discuss how this method is like and is different from the new-groups-below method, so this is a good mathematical conversation to support in the classroom. The "add tens into top number" method shown in figure 2.14 is easier than the new-groups-above method because you add the new ten into the top tens number and rewrite that number. Therefore, you just add the two numbers of tens that you see (6 tens and 3 tens). But some children confuse it with subtraction because a number is crossed out, so it is not as accessible as are the new-groups-below or show-all-totals methods shown in figure 2.13.

New groups above		Add tens into top numbers	
a.	$\overset{1}{5}8$ + 36 ——— 4	a.	$\overset{6}{\cancel{5}}8$ + 36 ——— 4
b.	$\overset{1}{5}8$ + 36 ——— 94	b.	$\overset{6}{\cancel{5}}8$ + 36 ——— 94

Fig. 2.14. General but more difficult methods for adding 2-digit numbers

If children do not invent the accessible and general show-all-totals and new-groups-below methods, they can be introduced by a teacher as a method that other children have used. Each method needs to be related to a math drawing and discussed and explained by the children, as do any methods that are used in the classroom.

Because counting on works so well to add single-digit numbers, some children invent extensions of counting on in which they count or add on tens or ones, always increasing the running total as they go. Several such methods are shown in figure 2.15. In the top-left method, the child uses ones from the second addend to make a decade number with the first addend (58 plus 2 is 60), then adds 3 tens, and then the remaining 4 ones from the second addend. The second method counts on by tens from the first addend and then adds the ones from the second addend. This requires knowing the patterns for counting on by tens from any number (e.g., 58, 68, 78, 88). The method at the bottom is a combination of the "add tens then add ones" method and counting on, in which the tens are added first and then the ones from each addend are added on to the running total. These methods work fine for the children who invent them. But some first and even second graders have difficulty correctly carrying out the number sequence counting patterns 58, 68, 78, 88 and the other counting or adding on that is involved. This becomes more problematic for children in grade 2 with three-digit addition where they may be adding on hundreds or tens or ones but saying a three-digit number each time (358 + 236 would be 358, 458, 558, 568, 578, 588, 590, 594 or 358, 458, 558, 568, 578, 588, 589, 590, 591, 592, 593, 594). Such sequence patterns become even more complex for problems with larger numbers of hundreds or tens. Many steps are involved for such problems. So these counting/adding-on methods are not general methods, and they involve counting patterns that are complex for some children.

The limitations of number lines for adding small numbers was discussed previously. Similar limitations apply for adding two-digit numbers. "Empty number lines" are a variation in which the 0 point is usually not marked, and the first number marked is often one of the addends. This version reduces number-line errors because there is not an extra mark for the 0. But then children are not necessarily using a number line; they are using a device that enables them to keep track of the cumulating total as it relates to parts of the second addend. These issues will be discussed in more detail in *Focus in Grade 2* (NCTM, forthcoming).

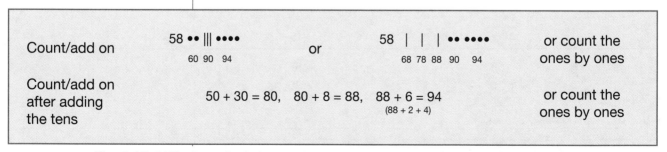

Fig. 2.15. Difficult methods for some/many children and very difficult for >3 digits

First graders who invent and can explain such counting/adding-on methods as shown in figure 2.15 of course should be allowed to use them. But it is important that general methods that generalize easily to three-digit and larger numbers be introduced and discussed. These general methods involve the most basic mathematical principle of addition: add like units and change to new units as needed. This principle applies to adding multidigit numbers, measurement systems, fractions (add like unit fractions), and decimals. Therefore children need to consider the mathematical concepts involved in the general methods shown in figure 2.13 and figure 2.14, but they certainly can benefit from the easier methods shown in figure 2.13.

After children have added two-digit numbers with regrouping, they can add any other combinations of single-digit and two-digit numbers including 2 two-digit numbers without regrouping. Two-digit subtraction with regrouping is too difficult for many first graders, so it is better to postpone any general subtraction work until grade 2. It is particularly important not to give two-digit subtraction problems with no regrouping (e.g., 65 − 42) because of the errors this induces in grade 2 (see figure 2.11). The very simple problems discussed initially to emphasize place values can be done in grade 1 (e.g., 90 − 7, 9 − 7, 90 − 70).

Understanding monetary values

The dime strips and nickel strips that can support understanding the values of dimes and nickels in kindergarten (see the top-right corner of figure 2.2) can also be used for first graders who need to understand the values of these coins as tens and as fives. First graders can practice their counts of tens-groups and counts of ones-groups by counting several dime strips using first the ten-penny side and then the dime side. They then can move on to counting mixed groups of dime strips and pennies, shifting from counting the dime strips by tens to counting the pennies by ones, just as they need to do when counting math drawings for two-digit numbers. Flashing ten fingers for each dime strip can also help children understand and use dimes as groups of ten. Only after children have this understanding of a dime as a group of ten pennies should they count collections of coins: dimes and pennies. Similarly, first graders can work with nickel strips until they have a firm understanding of a nickel as a group of five pennies. Combining pairs of nickels to make a dime where possible is a strategy that should be discussed. However, where an odd number of nickels is involved, children will still need to count a five. Shifting the counts from the count by tens to counts by five to counts by ones can be challenging. Having a student leader raise a hand and say "Stop! Shift!" can facilitate such shifts in counting initially. First graders do not need to deal with other coins. These shifts are complex enough, but they are consistent with the place-value work that first graders need to understand and can facilitate it. Children's understanding of the make-a-ten strategy can by supported by activities in which children are to make a dime when they add two groups of pennies that make a teen total: One addend can give pennies to the other addend to make ten pennies, which can be traded for a dime.

3 Geometry, Spatial Reasoning, and Measurement

Geometry, spatial reasoning, and measurement are important mathematical topics themselves and are also important in students' development of competence in other topics. That is, what students learn about geometric shapes and structures is significant for its own sake—these are core mathematical understandings and topics that are interesting to students. Furthermore, these topics are fundamental in students' learning of other mathematics, such as number, arithmetic, and patterns, as well as in describing the world around them. In its origin, *geometry* means "earth measure."

Spatial reasoning complements geometric knowledge. Spatial reasoning builds on two components: spatial orientation—knowing how to get around in the world—and spatial visualization—knowing how to build and manipulate objects mentally, including composing (putting together) and decomposing (taking apart) objects. Geometric measurement rounds out the core components.

Geometry, spatial reasoning, and measurement are interrelated, connect to other mathematics strands, and serve as foundations in connecting mathematics to real-world situations. For example, these core components are the bases of many models for arithmetic and other topics. Such geometric models include number lines, arrays (objects or squares arranged in rows and columns) in multiplication, and other models for fractions and algebraic structures. Spatial reasoning is also involved in graphing of all types. Spatial and geometric reasoning also lies at the heart of the study of physics, chemistry, biology, geology and geography, and art and architecture. Thus, across many areas and daily in the media, we see that a picture—or diagram or figure—can be "worth a thousand words." Increasing students' sophistication with visualization and imagery increases the meaning they can take from such pictures, including those seen daily on television, in videogames, and on GPS maps.

Unfortunately, geometry and measurement are topics in which U.S. students demonstrate their poorest performance in international comparisons. Fortunately, students have substantial intuitive knowledge that educators can build on; students can organize and build on this knowledge with good instruction; and they enjoy engaging with shapes, space, and measurements. Indeed, young students play with shapes and geometric structures naturally and frequently.

Geometry

In learning the geometry of shapes, students progress through increasingly powerful levels of thinking about shapes. For example, students can develop rich and more varied visual templates for the shape categories they know, learn about new shape categories, and eventually learn about the parts and attributes of the shapes. This is especially important if they have not yet received high-quality geometric experiences, because research suggests that, otherwise, concepts can tend to become inflexible by the end of first grade.

Table 3.1 presents the developmental progressions for ideas and skills for geometry and spatial reasoning.

Shape and structure

First graders form and tend to initially rely on visual templates, or models, of shape categories. For example, students recognize a square because "it looks like" other squares. Unfortunately, many students have experienced shapes named as squares only when they have a horizontal base, a base parallel to the bottom of the page. Therefore, many believe that a square that is rotated 45 degrees from the horizontal is no longer a square but is a diamond. Students' visual images of shape categories such as rectangle and especially triangle are too often even

Table 3.1

Progression of Ideas and Skills for Geometry, Spatial Reasoning, and Measurement

Kindergarten	Grade 1	Grade 2
Shape and Structure	**Shape and Structure**	**Shape and Structure**
Recognize and describe a wide variety of two-dimensional shapes (e.g., octagons, parallelograms, convex/concave figures) regardless of orientation, size, and shape. Sort shapes by number of sides and/or corners and length relationships between sides. Recognize and name common three-dimensional shapes (including real-world objects), including spheres, cylinders, [rectangular] prisms, and pyramids.	Name most common shapes, including rhombuses, without making such mistakes as calling ovals circles. Recognize (at least) right angles, so distinguish between a rectangle and a parallelogram without right angles. Use manipulatives representing parts of shapes, such as sides and angle "connectors," to make a shape that is completely correct on the basis of knowledge of components and relationships.	Identify shapes in terms of their components. Use length measurement of sides to determine properties of shapes (e.g., marking unit lengths on sides of shapes and counting the units, finding and connecting midpoints of sides of different shapes to see the two composed shapes). Recognize and describe contexts in which angle knowledge is relevant, including corners (can discuss "sharper" angles), crossings (e.g., a scissors), and, later, bent objects and bends (sometimes bends in paths and slopes). (These relate to the measurement goals.)
Spatial Relations	**Spatial Relations**	**Spatial Relations and Compositions and Decompositions in Space**
Begin to use relational language of *right* and *left*. Identify and create symmetric figures (e.g., use mirrors for reflections).	Use geometric motions to create symmetric figures (e.g., paper folding; also using mirrors for reflections) and determine congruence.	Construct and duplicate units of units (shapes made from other shapes) intentionally; understand each as being both multiple small shapes *and* one larger shape. For example, understand a rectangular array of squares as consisting of rows of a given number, equal to the number of columns. Continue a pattern of shapes that leads to a tiling or tessellation. (These relate to the measurement goals.)
Compositions and Decompositions in Space	**Compositions and Decompositions in Space**	
Create pattern block designs (those with multiples of 60-degree and 120-degree angles). Create compositions and complete puzzles with systematicity and anticipation by using a variety of shape sets (e.g., pattern blocks; rectangular grids with squares, right triangles, and rectangles; tangrams). Build simple three-dimensional structures from pictured models.	Make new two-dimensional shapes and shape structures out of smaller shapes and substitute groups of shapes for other shapes to create new shapes in different ways. (See related area goals.)	

(*Continued on next page*)

Table 3.1

Progression of Ideas and Skills for Geometry, Spatial Reasoning, and Measurement (continued)

Kindergarten	Grade 1	Grade 2
Concept of Measurement	**Concept of Measurement**	**Concept of Measurement**
Use measurable attributes, such as length or area, to solve problems by comparing and ordering objects.	Compose and decompose plane and solid shapes, thus building an understanding of part-whole relationships and developing the background for working with units composed of units. (These relate to the geometry goals.)	Extend concepts of measurement for length and area as described below.
Length	**Length**	**Length**
Compare the lengths of two objects both directly (by comparing them with each other) and indirectly (by comparing both with a third object), and order several objects according to length (even if differences between consecutive lengths are small). Measure by laying units end-to-end, covering the whole without gaps, and count the units to find the total length.	Measure by repeated use of a unit, and apply the resulting measures to comparison situations.	Understand linear measure as an iteration of units, and use rulers with that understanding. Understand the need for equal-length units, at least intuitively and/or in some situations. Recognize that different units will result in different measures. Relate size and number of units explicitly, understanding that the smaller the unit, the more iterations are needed to cover a given length. Understand the need for and use standard units of length (centimeter, inch). Use simple unit rulers accurately with minimal guidance. Add two lengths to obtain the length of a whole. Relate rulers, bar graphs, and number lines as length models involving unit lengths from 0 to a given number.
Area	**Area**	**Area**
Cover a rectangular region with square units. Count squares in rectangular arrays correctly and (increasingly) systematically.	Make and draw coverings of simple rectangular regions with square units. For rectangles two squares high or wide, count the rows or columns of two by twos.	Draw parallel lines to subdivide small rectangles into squares rather than draw individual squares (see corresponding geometric shape composition/decomposition goals). Count squares in rectangles by ones by row or by column. For 2s and 5s, skip-count by row or by column.
Volume	**Volume**	**Volume**
Compare two containers using a third container and (at least implicitly) transitive reasoning. Fill rectangular containers with cubes and/or make rectangular prisms ("buildings") from layers of blocks.	Fill rectangular containers with cubes, completing one layer at a time with cubes, and/or make rectangular prisms ("buildings") from layers of blocks.	Construct and duplicate units of units, identifying repeated layers of cubes in rectangular prisms made of cubes.

Note: Some composition and decomposition activities overlap with measurement (area and volume). Grade 3 develops the above area work as a setting for multiplication. Fuller development of area is a grade 4 Focal Point, and fuller development of volume is a grade 5 Focal Point.

more limited, as they exclude many possibilities that are valid members of each category (see figure 3.1). To ensure that students form accurate and rich mental images, they need to experience a variety of shapes in each shape category in varied orientations so that their mental models are not overly restricted.

Students should then compare shapes in each category with paired shapes that appear similar but do not have one of the important defining attributes (see figure 3.2). Teachers can ask students to compare the shapes and describe

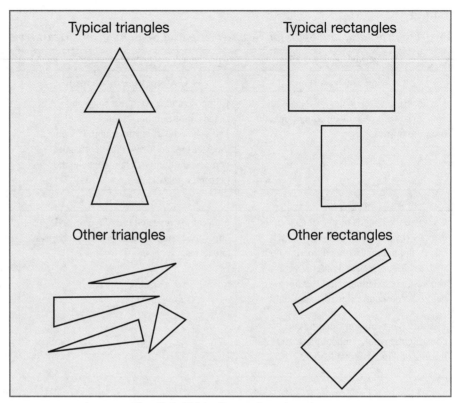

Fig. 3.1. Triangles and rectangles

and discuss how they are different. Such focus on one attribute at a time helps students abstract and describe that attribute and separate defining attributes from those attributes that do *not* define a shape category (e.g., its position or orientation, size, or color). Development of flexible, accurate "visual thinking" should continue throughout students' education, even as more mathematically explicit and sophisticated levels of thinking and language take precedence.

Students also need to see examples of shapes beyond the familiar few. Without these, students develop limited notions. For example, many students come to believe incorrectly that a geometry figure such as a trapezoid "is not a shape" because it is not a shape for which they know a name (often they know only circle, square, triangle, and rectangle). Students can learn to recognize not only trapezoids but also such shapes as rhombuses, hexagons, octagons, and parallelograms. Figure 3.3 provides information for the teacher about many two-dimensional (2D) geometric shapes. The term "2D shapes" means flat shapes (e.g., plane shapes that can be drawn in their entirety on paper) that are *closed*, meaning that they have no "loose, dangling ends," and are *connected*, meaning they are in one single piece and do not have sides that cross each other. Figure 3.4 examines the concept of a right angle, which is needed in describing rectangles. Figure 3.5 provides information for the teacher about relationships among types of shapes.

For several reasons, students must go beyond naming shapes to understanding their attributes. First, such descriptive activity encourages children to move beyond visual prototypes to the use of *mathematical* criteria. Second, discussions redirect children's attention and build strong concepts, mutually

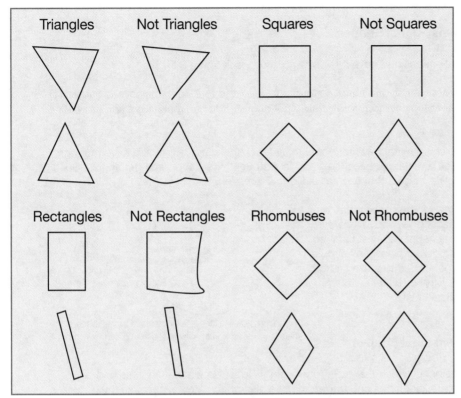

Fig. 3.2. Shape examples and nonexamples

affecting and benefiting mental images. Third, children find these activities interesting, and the activities engage first graders in mathematical conversations.

With rich activities and teacher questioning, students can develop explicit and sophisticated levels of thinking and communication in discussing shapes. They can learn to describe, and even define, these shapes in terms of their attributes (properties). They can build accurate representations of shapes from physical models of line segments such as straws, connecting them with balls of clay or pipe cleaners. As they discuss what they have built, attributes of the shapes will arise naturally. Students can be asked to justify why their construction fits the definition of a certain shape category. They may say that what they build is a rectangle *because* it has two pairs of sides that are equal in length and all right angles. Such activity helps students begin to understand the *geometric structure* of all rectangles at an explicit level of thinking. It encourages students to view shapes analytically.

Symmetry is an important topic in all of mathematics and especially in geometry. People use symmetry consistently, at all ages. For example, symmetric shapes are detected faster, discriminated more accurately, and often remembered better than asymmetrical shapes. However, many concepts of symmetry are not developed without explicit instruction. When guided by the teacher, first graders can discuss and use such ideas, identifying symmetry not only in shapes such as rectangles but in their environment. They can design and extend symmetry into their block buildings and art work.

In art work or work with shape sets such as pattern blocks, students use and can analyze and discuss different types of symmetry. Plane figures have *line*, or *mirror*, symmetry when their shape is reversed on opposite sides of a

Definitions of Familiar Two-Dimensional Shapes

Triangles are those two-dimensional shapes that have three straight sides (see figure 3.2).

Rectangles are those two-dimensional shapes that have four straight sides and four right angles (see figure 3.1). Corners of standard pieces of paper are usually (approximately) right angles. You can make right angles using doublefolding (see figure 3.4).

Squares are those two-dimensional shapes that have four straight sides of the same length and have four right angles. Notice that any square is also a rectangle because it has four straight sides and four right angles. So squares could be defined as special rectangles that have all sides the same length.

Informally, circles are those two-dimensional shapes that are "perfectly round." From a mathematical perspective, however, circle are those two-dimensional shapes that consist of all points that are a fixed distance from a fixed center point. Any simple tool (such as a compass or even a pencil tied to a fixed length of string) that holds a pencil point a fixed distance away from a center point will draw a circle, as shown here.

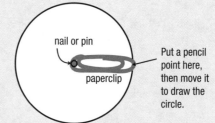

nail or pin

paperclip

Put a pencil point here, then move it to draw the circle.

A circle consists of all the locations that are a fixed distance (here: a paperclip length) away from a fixed point (here: the nail).

Definitions of Other Two-Dimensional Shapes

Quadrilaterals are those two-dimensional shapes that have four straight sides. Notice that squares and rectangles (as well as rhombuses, parallelograms, and trapezoids) are also quadrilaterals because these shapes have four straight sides.

Rhombuses are those two-dimensional shapes that have four straight sides of the same length. Notice that every square is also a rhombus because it has four sides of the same length.

Parallelograms are those two-dimensional shapes that have four straight sides and for which each pair of opposite sides are parallel. Informally, two straight sides are parallel if it is possible to slide one without turning so that both lie on the same straight line. Or two are parallel if when both are extended to become infinitely long straight lines, they never meet.

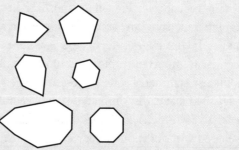

Trapezoids are those two-dimensional shapes that have four straight sides and at least one pair of parallel sides. (Some people define trapezoids as those two-dimensional shapes that have four straight sides and exactly one pair of parallel sides.)

Pentagons are those two-dimensional shapes that have five straight sides.

Hexagons are those two-dimensional shapes that have six straight sides.

Octagons are those two-dimensional shapes that have eight straight sides.

Polygons are closed shapes with all straight sides. All the shapes above except for circles are polygons. There are names for many other polygons, but they are often referred to with simple numbers (e.g., a polygon with 13 sides can be called a "13-gon"). Often the *regular polygons*—those with all sides the same length and all angles the same size—are more familiar. The pentagon, hexagon, and octagon on the right in the illustrations above are regular polygons. Equilateral triangles and squares are regular polygons with three and four sides, respectively.

Fig. 3.3. Definitions of shapes for teachers

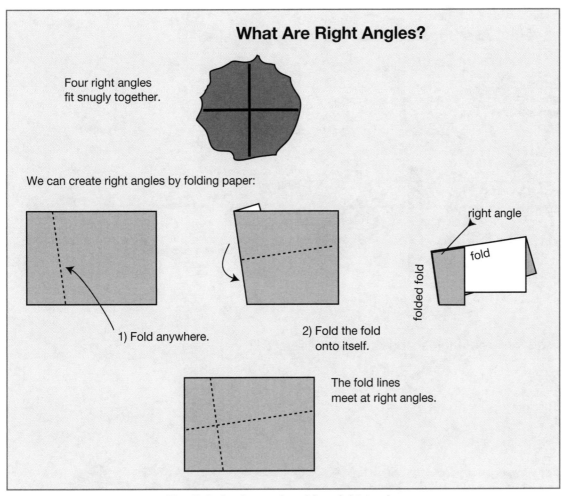

What Are Right Angles?

Four right angles fit snugly together.

We can create right angles by folding paper:

1) Fold anywhere.

2) Fold the fold onto itself.

folded fold

right angle

fold

The fold lines meet at right angles.

Fig. 3.4. Seeing and making right angles

line. A figure has *rotational* symmetry when it can be turned less than a full turn to fit on itself exactly. Ideas about line symmetry can be developed by folding, by folding and cutting paper, or by exploring with a mirror. Rotational symmetry can be illustrated by rotating one copy of a figure so it fits exactly on another copy. In both cases, emphasize that a symmetric figure is congruent with itself. That is, sides of equal length correspond with one another, as do angles of equal size.

Computer-based activities can also contribute to students' thinking about shapes, their components, and their relationships to other shapes. Their advantages include greater control and flexibility, as well as linking the visual to the symbolic and abstract. (See figure 3.6 for an example. Remember, too, that other computer programs can serve similar purposes and that one can act out such situations with children alone—one child is the "tracer" and others give him or her commands to go forward, turn right, etc.)

Too often, U.S. students are not introduced to such strong, conceptual geometric experiences. Teachers and curriculum writers may assume that students in primary-grade classrooms have little knowledge of geometric figures. Further, teachers may have had few rich experiences with geometry in their own education or professional development. Thus, it is not surprising that many classrooms exhibit limited geometry instruction. We can and must do better.

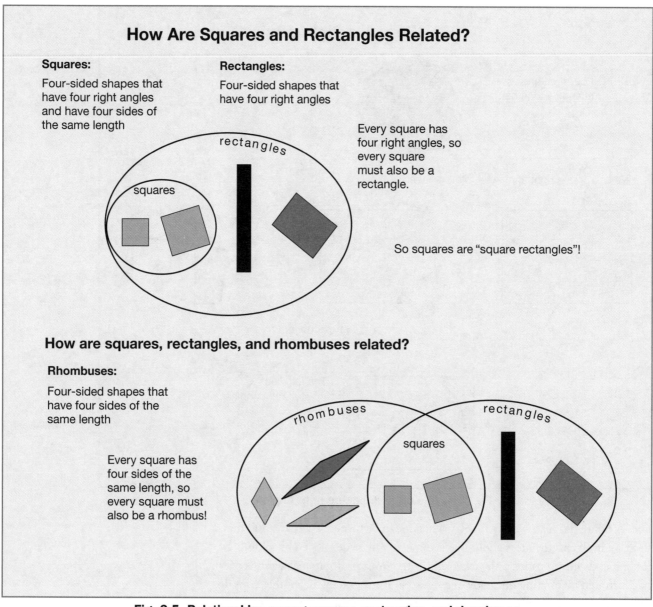

How Are Squares and Rectangles Related?

Squares:

Four-sided shapes that have four right angles and have four sides of the same length

Rectangles:

Four-sided shapes that have four right angles

Every square has four right angles, so every square must also be a rectangle.

So squares are "square rectangles"!

How are squares, rectangles, and rhombuses related?

Rhombuses:

Four-sided shapes that have four sides of the same length

Every square has four sides of the same length, so every square must also be a rhombus!

Fig. 3.5. Relationships among squares, rectangles, and rhombuses

A final type of relationship between shapes is also important. Students should learn to describe the differences between two-dimensional (2D, or "flat") and three-dimensional (3D) shapes—and relate the two. Children typically come to school with many more experiences with 3D shapes than 2D shapes in their personal world. They can also learn the mathematical names for familiar 3D shapes, such as spheres (balls), cylinders (cans), prisms (boxes), and pyramids. Faces of 3D shapes can be identified as specific 2D shapes—for example, by tracing around the faces of boxes and blocks of various shapes. They might trace around all the faces of each type of 3D shape on separate pieces of paper, then challenge one another to figure out which set of 2D shapes are the faces of each 3D shape. They can understand and discuss properties such as parallel faces in some contexts, such as building with blocks—where geometric and spatial structures are especially important. This is one type of spatial relation, a topic to which we turn.

Spatial relations

Reasoning about spatial relations includes two main spatial abilities: spatial orientation and spatial visualization and imagery. Other important competencies include knowing how to represent spatial ideas and how and when to use such spatial knowledge in solving problems.

Spatial orientation involves knowing where you are and how to get around in the world. Similar to number, spatial orientation is a core cognitive domain—humans have spatial competencies from birth. Students' skills are initially based on their own position and their movements through space and soon increasingly include external references. Students should understand and use spatial terms including difficult relational terms such as "right" and "left" in both three-dimensional and two-dimensional contexts. The key for educators is helping children *mathematize* these early competencies.

Spatial visualization involves building and manipulating objects mentally. Images are mental representations of objects that are structurally similar to their real-world counterparts. An image is not a "picture in the head." It is more abstract, more malleable, and less crisp than a picture. It is often segmented into parts. The spatial visualization considered here involves understanding and performing imagined movements of two- and three-dimensional geometric objects. Students need to be able to create a mental image and manipulate it.

Although many activities develop both these spatial abilities, we focus on each of them in turn. To develop *spatial orientation*, students might walk a path, remembering or drawing how they moved, and then try to make the Logo turtle move along a similar path on the video screen. The commands might be "FD 100, RT 90, FD 150, RT 90, FD 100, RT 90, FD 150, RT 90" (as a spatial visualization task, can you imagine what the shape would be *before* viewing figure 3.6?).

This type of work can be connected to creating maps that include geometric correspondences—for example, objects in a line in the classroom should be in a line on the map. First, students often need to learn more about perspective. For example, they might identify block structures from various viewpoints, matching photographs of the same structure that are portrayed from different perspectives: "Where did the photographer stand to take *this* picture?" Experiences with technological tools can help build these skills. For example, teachers might try to use Google Maps or other similar Internet-based tools to "zoom in and out" so students see dynamically the relation of the school to the surrounding environment. Teachers might help students similarly view their own houses. Parents might be encouraged to help their students relate movements in a car to the maps and directions of GPS systems.

Work with students to raise four mathematical questions: direction—which way?, distance—how far?, location—where?, and identification—what objects? To answer these questions, students need to develop a variety of skills. Students must learn to deal with mapping processes of abstraction, generalization, and symbolization. As an example of *identification*, competent map readers know that some map symbols are icons, such as an airplane for an airport, but others are more abstract, such as circles for cities. In contrast, young students often believe that the airplane represents "one large plane" or that a road really is red. To work with symbolization, students might first build with objects such as model buildings, then draw pictures of the objects' arrangements, then use maps that are "miniaturizations" and those that use abstract symbols.

As they use their maps, students can apply the previously learned navigation ideas, such as front, back, distance, direction, and turning. For example, they might make a map of the school yard and give directions to a secret location (e.g., "start at the monkey bars. Head north. Walk 20 feet (etc.).... Where are you?").

Equity in the education of spatial thinking is an important issue. Some studies indicate that teachers of primary-grade students spend more time with boys than girls and usually interact with boys in the block, construction, sand play, and climbing areas and with girls in the dramatic play area. Also, boys engage in spatial activities more than girls at home, both alone and with caretakers. Such differences may interact with biology to account for early spatial skill advantages for boys. Fortunately, well-planned activities in first grade can

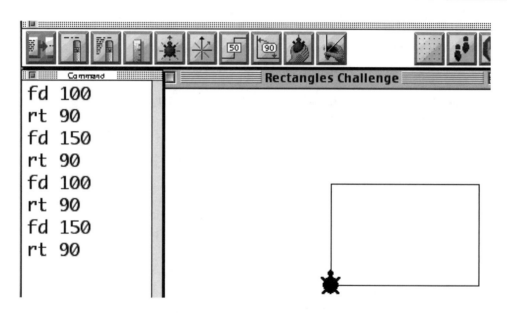

Using Logo "turtle graphics" to describe and draw rectangles

First graders enjoy and learn from work with Logo's "turtle graphics," in which they program the turtle to draw with geometric commands, such as FORWARD 100 (or FD 100) and RIGHT 90 (RT 90) (that is, turn to the right 90 degrees). Research indicates that they particularly benefit from exploring squares and rectangles. Further, this work can *connect* number and place-value understandings with those of geometry and measurement. Here, for example, students used the Logo turtle to draw a rectangle. After all students completed a rectangle, the teacher asked them how they planned to draw a rectangle and then, how they *know* it is a rectangle on the basis of the Logo program (e.g., that opposite sides are equal in length because they were drawn by the same "forward" or "fd" command). They discussed what was the same about all the programs and the rectangles they produced, and what differed. They discussed for a long time one pair's procedure that used the same input, or number, for all four forward commands. That procedure produced a square. They eventually called it a "square-rectangle."

Fig. 3.6. A Logo turtle's path

provide all students with strong spatial competencies, and it is important for teachers to do so. For example, teachers should make sure girls walk through large spaces around school and map these spaces. Also, they should encourage girls to engage in these activities and interact with them as they do. Further, to *mathematize* such experience with boys or girls, teachers need to incorporate mathematical terms and concepts into these interactions. For example, teachers might ask girls to build a bridge with blocks over the river they have made or to build complex levels in a castle—not just "walls." Such experiences close the spatial skills gaps that may separate girls and boys.

Students begin to learn to *structure space* as they attempt to cover a rectangular space with square tiles. Counting those tiles provides a useful connection to number and practice on systematically keeping track of which objects have been counted. Students often count arrays as shown in figures 3.7a and 3.7b. Discussions can help them learn and practice more systematic strategies such as shown in figure 3.7c.

To develop spatial visualization abilities, first graders—like all young students—should have many experiences manipulating shapes. One valuable type of activity is putting shapes together to make other shapes—this is the focus of the next section and will be discussed there. Another example is a version of the mental visualization activity "snapshots"—the teacher secretly builds a shape out of toothpicks or straws, shows it to students for two seconds, then

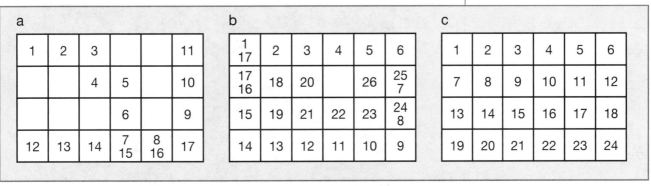

Fig. 3.7. Students' methods for counting tiles in a concrete array

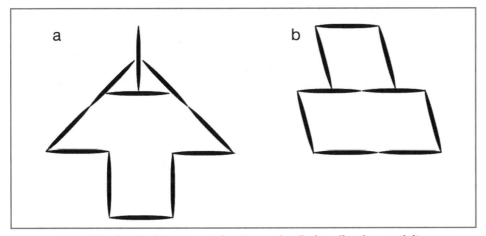

Fig. 3.8. Toothpick shapes for "snapshot" visualization activity

covers it. Students build a copy. The teacher then reveals the original, and students discuss what they saw and what they attempted to build. These shapes can start simple but get quite complex and lead to good discussions on what was seen (figure 3.8a). The teacher encourages students to use geometric properties of shapes to guide the discussion and to direct students' attention to such properties in future tasks. In figure 3.8b, for example, recognition of parallelism aids accurate copying.

In addition to these physical experiences, technological games, tools, and simulations can be helpful in developing spatial visualization abilities. Some worthwhile computer activities and games include simple maps and directions, and work with the Logo turtle was already described. Other technology tools include manipulatives that students move using computer screen tools. When students use such tools—for example, to slide, turn, and flip shapes—these geometric motions become more accessible to reflection, and so students learn about them more explicitly. For example, when students try to duplicate a figure on the computer screen, they have to explicitly choose how to slide or turn the components of the shapes. Figure 3.9 provides an example of a simple problem that involves building shapes from parts. The following section includes examples of manipulating shapes as regions.

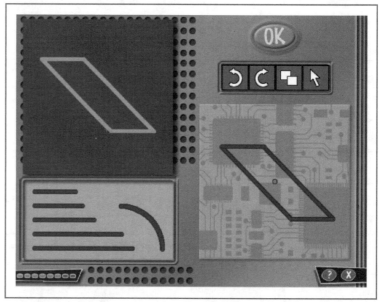

Fig. 3.9. Building a shape from parts. Students see the model of a shape they have to build (to "fix a computer") in the upper-left region, and they assemble the shape in the lower-right region, using the parts and tools provided.

Compositions and decompositions in space

The abilities involved in putting together and taking apart shapes are important for many reasons. These geometric competencies are at the foundation of geometry, but also arithmetic (e.g., composing and decomposing numbers and arrays in multiplication), measurement, and higher-order geometric work, as well as such fields as architecture and the visual arts. Creating and then iterating units and higher-order units in the context of constructing patterns, measuring, and computing are established bases for mathematical understanding and analysis.

At first grade especially, students' composing and decomposing geometric units connects with, and mutually supports, their composing and decomposing numerical units. For example, in learning single-digit addition combinations, students are composing and decomposing numbers from 0 to 18. They also learn to compose 10 ones to be a *unit* of ten and compose and decompose numbers to 100 into units (tens and ones).

This connection is a main reason that composing and decomposing geometric shapes is a Curriculum Focal Point for grade 1 students. Further, this already supports learning of other geometric and measurement competencies. *Curriculum Focal Points* (NCTM 2006) says that as first graders "combine figures, they recognize them from different perspectives and orientations, describe their geometric attributes and properties, and determine how they are alike and different, in the process developing a background for measurement and initial understandings of such properties as congruence and symmetry" (p. 13).

Studies have shown that students may receive inadequate instruction in geometry—especially in the domain of composing and decomposing shapes. For example, one teacher overgeneralized in saying, "Every time you put two triangles together, you get a square." Under what conditions is this statement true? Can you figure out several shapes that could be constructed? Be sure to think about the different kinds of triangles. Then keep reading and see if you recognize your solution.

Teachers have rarely had opportunities to explore and build sufficient geometric understanding themselves. Exploring open-ended questions is valuable for teachers and their students. For example, "Let's cut a square with a straight cut from one vertex to the opposite vertex. What do we get? Are these two triangles congruent (or identical)? Let's use the triangle as our unit. What *different* ways can we put the two units back together with full sides touching? What shapes will we get? If you make a shape that is turned a different way, should we consider it the same or a different shape?" (See figure 3.10.)

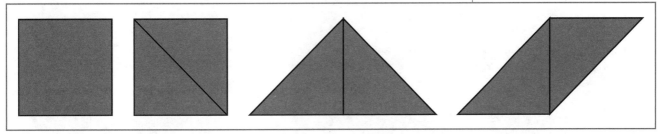

Fig. 3.10. Decomposing a square into two right triangles and recomposing the triangles in different ways

Students can develop the ability to intentionally and systematically combine shapes to make new shapes and complete puzzles. They do so with increasing anticipation on the basis of the shapes' attributes, and thus they develop mental imagery of the component shapes. That is, they can learn first to put shapes together to make pictures, first with a bit of trial and error (figure 3.11a) and increasingly by accurately predicting the placement of each piece using visualization and knowledge of geometric properties (figure 3.11b). They then move to the level of thinking where they can intentionally and systematically substitute one composition of shapes for another. In Figure 3.12a, the puzzle looks easy, but when students have succeeded building one solution, the software asks for another—different—solution.

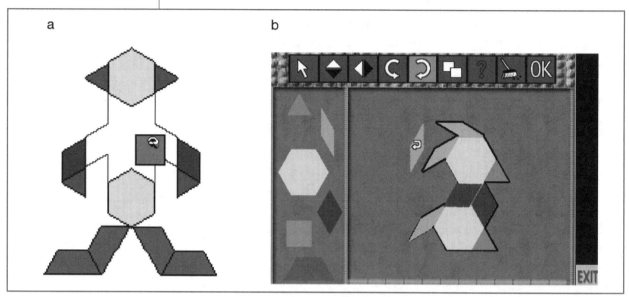

Fig. 3.11. Composing shapes to make new shapes

In Figure 3.12b, children are building all the possible ways to make a hexagon from the pattern block set. They can begin to talk about their solutions. If you use just one shape—one unit—how many of that unit does it take to fill a hexagon?

As a side note, Figure 3.11a also illustrates that computers can help students become aware of and mathematize their actions. For example, students can move physical puzzle pieces into place at a young age, but usually they do

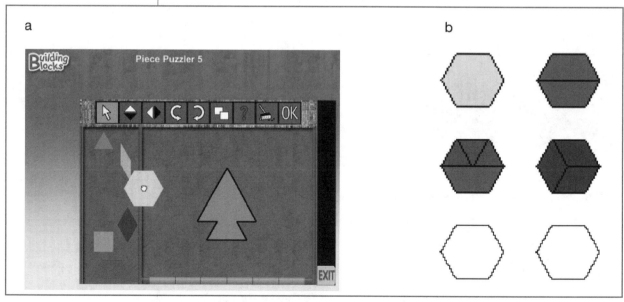

Fig. 3.12. Composing shapes in several different ways

not reflect on their actions. Using computer tools, however, can help students become aware of and describe these motions. Figures 3.11b and 3.12a illustrate the use of tools that slide, flip, and turn shapes. Intentional use of these tools brings these geometric motions to an explicit level of awareness for students.

Thus, instructional aids support learning because they are manipulatable and meaningful. Therefore, computer tools and games can provide representations that are just as real and helpful to young children as physical manipulatives. In fact, they may have specific advantages. As another example, some computer manipulatives offer more flexibility than their non-computer counterparts. Computer-based pattern blocks, for example, can be decomposed in more ways than physical pattern blocks. Further, students and teachers can save and later retrieve any arrangement of computer manipulatives. Similarly, computers allow us to store more than static configurations. They can record and replay *sequences* of our actions on manipulatives. Doing so helps young children form dynamic images.

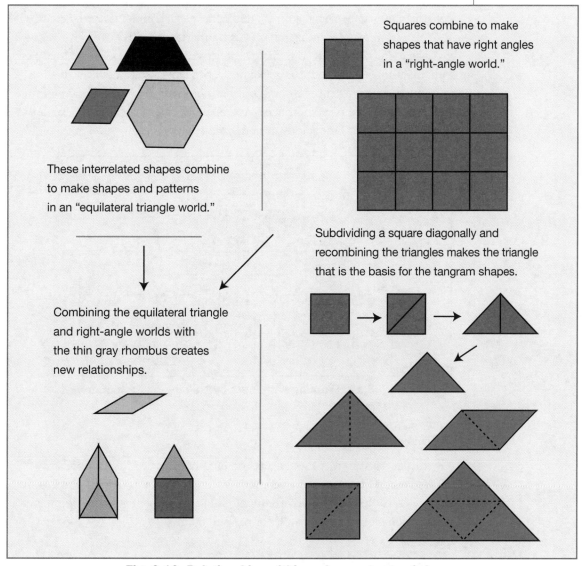

Squares combine to make shapes that have right angles in a "right-angle world."

These interrelated shapes combine to make shapes and patterns in an "equilateral triangle world."

Subdividing a square diagonally and recombining the triangles makes the triangle that is the basis for the tangram shapes.

Combining the equilateral triangle and right-angle worlds with the thin gray rhombus creates new relationships.

Fig. 3.13. Relationships within and among sets of shapes

Children make a significant advance when they can combine shapes with different properties, extending the pattern block shapes (whose angles are multiples of 30 degrees) common at early levels to shapes such as tangrams (angles that are multiples of 45 degrees), and with sets of various shapes that include angles that are multiples of 15 degrees, as well as sections of circles. Combining these shape sets should be done after students have worked with the pattern block shapes separately from the square/rectangle/right triangle shapes based on 90 degrees and 45 degrees because many compositions are possible when the angles are consistent. Figure 3.13 shows the shapes in these various sets and how they depend on angles.

Using 3D shapes, students can learn to build complex structures with units. Many children may have experiences building with blocks, Legos, and other sets at home or in earlier educational environments. As an advanced example, the block building in figure 3.14 has the basic unit of an arch. You can also see an "arch of arches" and how it uses several of these "units of units" in its construction. First graders with rich backgrounds of playing and analyzing geometric constructions can be challenged to build up from such units, at first by constructing them from pictures or diagrams (this translation from 2D to 3D is already a valuable skill), and then from more abstract verbal descriptions (e.g., "make a building using at least four complex units"). Students also can build structures with interconnecting cubes from 2D pictures of these structures. Building from the instructions from geometric toys and manipulatives such as Lego, Anchor Stones, K'Nex, and Googolplex at home and school can help develop these skills.

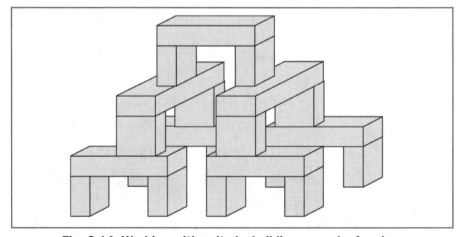

Fig. 3.14. Working with units by building an arch of arches

Measurement

Geometric measurement[1] connects and enriches the two most important topics for early mathematics, geometry and number, in a way that focuses students' descriptions of our environment. Table 3.1 presents the developmental progressions for ideas and skills for measurement.

---

1 In this section, we describe students' development of *geometric* measurement—measurement in one, two, and three dimensions. We do not consider measurement of nongeometric attributes, such as weight/mass, capacity, time, and color, because these are more appropriately considered in science and social studies curricula.

Measurement can be defined as the process of assigning a number to a magnitude of some attribute of an object, such as its length, area, or volume, relative to a unit, such as the length of the room in meters. These attributes are continuous quantities. Measurement's continuous quantities are amounts that can always be divided into smaller and smaller subunits, such as meters, centimeters, millimeters, micrometers (a millionth of a meter), and so forth.

First graders also can learn important measurement concepts. Many U.S. students show limited understanding of measurement until *after* the primary grades. This is not an age or "developmental" limitation, however, but a sign of limited, ineffective experiences with, and teaching of, measurement.

Length

Length is a characteristic of an object or path found by quantifying how far it is between endpoints of the object. "Distance" is often used similarly to quantify how far it is between two points in space. Measuring length or distance consists of two aspects, identifying a unit of measure and subdividing the object by that unit: placing that unit repeatedly from one end to the other (*iterating* the unit) alongside the object (or placing multiple copies of that unit alongside).

Some concepts and skills concern comparing and ordering lengths without assigning numbers to them. For example, one can compare the height of a table and a chair by placing them next to each other and comparing these lengths directly. Not every direct comparison is so easy, of course—the bottom endpoints of the table and chair are "automatically" aligned—and students should learn to make such direct comparisons with any objects.

In situations where direct comparison is not possible or convenient, indirect comparison can be used. Students can learn to compare the length of two objects using a third object and transitive reasoning. For example, they can figure out that one path from the teacher's desk to the door is longer than another because the first path is longer than a piece of string but the other is shorter than that string. Ideas of transitivity can then be explicitly discussed: If A is longer than B and B is longer than C, then A must be longer than C as well.

Ordering a set of objects extends this set of skills and understandings. Such sequencing requires multiple comparisons. To complete the task efficiently also requires a systematic strategy, such as moving each new object "down the line" to see where it fits. Students can be challenged to order, or seriate, sets of lengths that are sufficiently similar in length and numerous (e.g., a set of sticks whose measures are 12, 13, 14, … 20 cm in length) so they develop such systematic strategies and learn that in an ordered series, each stick must be longer than all those on one "side" of it and shorter than all those on the other side.

Such reasoning is important mathematically, and useful in many contexts, but it is not true *measurement* until students assign a number to length. This has the additional benefit of beginning to connect number to continuous quantities, such as the length of a room being about 7 meters and the area of its floor being about 35 square meters (m^2). Such connections help build not just measurement concepts but new mental models that teachers and students can use to develop number and arithmetic meanings.

First graders can learn to understand combining lengths explicitly. For example, they can add two lengths to obtain the length of the whole. They can use a simple unit ruler to (or put a length of connecting cubes together that) measure one plasticine "snake" and measure the length of another "snake" to find the total of their lengths. Or, more practically, they can measure all the sides of a table with unmarked (foot) rulers to measure how much ribbon they would need to decorate the perimeter of the table. Their use of rows or columns in covering a rectangular area also implies at least an implicit composition of units into a composite unit.

First graders can learn to measure with the repeated use of a unit. However, they initially may not be precise in such iterations. Students can learn to lay physical units such as paper clips or centimeter or inch manipulatives end to end and count them to measure a length. Especially if they have not had high-quality educational experiences previously, some may initially iterate a unit leaving gaps between subsequent units or overlapping adjacent units. For these children, measuring may be a physical activity of placing units along a path in some manner rather than the activity of *covering* the space/ length of the object with no gaps. As with transitive reasoning tasks, using comparison tasks and comparing students' results with one another can help reveal the limitations of such procedures and promote the need for more accurate measuring. Students especially enjoy correcting inaccurate measurements that the teacher might purposely make (see figure 3.15). Teachers can have children tell in a precise and elaborate manner *what* the problem is, *why* it leads to incorrect measurements, and *how* to fix it and measure accurately.

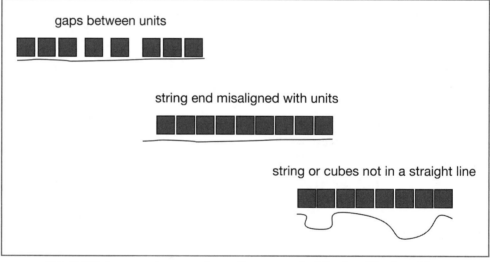

Fig. 3.15. Inaccurate procedures for measuring the length of a string

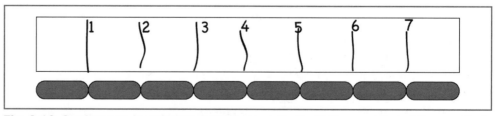

Fig. 3.16. Students make rulers to help them understand the meaning of the markings

Students should then measure with manipulative units using standard units of length, such as centimeters or inches. Label these as "length-units" with the students. As they measure with these manipulatives, discuss the concepts and skills involved (e.g., as previously discussed, not leaving space between successive length-units). Students can construct simple unit rulers by marking off a length-unit such as inches on strips of paper (see figure 3.16). Thus, students' first rulers should be simply ways to help count the iteration of length-units. Frequently comparing results of measuring the same object with manipulatives and these rulers helps students connect their experiences and ideas.

Similarly, discussions might frequently focus on *"What* are you counting?" with the answer being "length-units" or "centimeters" or the like. This is especially important because counting discrete items often convinces students that the size of things you are counting does not matter (there could be exactly 10 toys, even if they are different sizes). In contrast, for measurement, unit size is critical, so plan experiences and reflections on the use of units in various discrete counting and measurement contexts. See below.

Teacher:	Let me ask you two questions. I think I can fool you on at least one.
Children:	No!
Teacher:	I think I can. Look at the blue [inch] cubes and red [cm] cubes I have here. Are there more blue cubes or more red cubes, or do both sets have the same number?
Child 1:	That's *easy.* There are five blue cubes and eight red cubes. So there are more red cubes.
Teacher:	But the blue cubes are bigger!
Child 2:	That doesn't matter when you count.
Teacher:	OK, I'll get you with my second question. If I lined up all the blue cubes and then lined up all the red cubes, which line would be longer?
Children:	Blue!
Child 3:	No, red, right?
Children:	(Others respond:) Blue! They're longer!
Teacher:	See, I *did* fool you. How can five be longer than eight?
Child 3:	See, I told you. It's red.
Children:	(Most:) No, blue. She said *longer.* Not more, like counting each cube!
Teacher:	I'm confused now. Who can explain it?
Child 4:	You gotta use the *length-unit.* Because five blue length-units is *longer* than eight red length-units. See? (lines them up).

After further discussion, the class agrees. The teacher names the blue length-units as inches and the red length-units as centimeters and restates the comparison in these units. (Five blue *inches* are longer than eight red *centimeters.*) She then helps children summarize that you must know and say the units when you are comparing.

Finally, first graders may explore the concept of the inverse relationship between the size of the unit of length and the number of units required to cover a specific length or distance, recognizing it at least at an intuitive level (this is developed explicitly in grade 2). For example, it will take more centimeter lengths to cover a certain distance than inch lengths because inches are the larger unit. However, first graders may not appreciate the need for identical units. Previously described work with manipulative units of standard measure (e.g., 1 inch or 1 cm), along with related use of rulers and consistent discussion, will help children learn both the concepts and procedures of linear measurement.

Area

The area of a region (a portion, or subset, of a plane, such as a rectangle and its interior) is a measure of the amount of space inside it; it tells us how much material is needed to cover the region (see figure 3.17). Area measurement assumes that a suitable two-dimensional region is chosen as a unit, congruent regions have equal areas, regions do not overlap, and the area of the union of two regions that do not overlap is the sum of their areas. Finding the area of a region can be thought of as tiling a region with a two-dimensional unit of measure. To understand area effectively, students need to develop spatial structuring—the mental operation of organizing space into rows and columns. Such understandings are complex, and students develop them over time. These area understandings do not develop well in traditional U.S. instruction and have not for a long time because students do not get experience in such spatial work.

It is somewhat surprising that students need to learn to *structure an array* —a rectangular arrangement of squares—into rows and columns. Often people believe that students should just be able to "see it." However, seeing the *structure* takes time, and ensuring that first graders can cover a rectangular space with physical tiles systematically and talk about what they have done lays a good foundation for more sophisticated understandings that develop later.

In later grades, understanding area requires seeing how to decompose shapes into parts and how to move and recombine the parts to make simpler

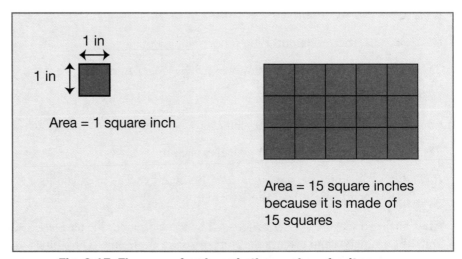

Fig. 3.17. The area of a shape is the number of unit squares it takes to cover the shape without gaps or overlaps.

shapes whose areas are already known. First graders learn the foundations of such procedures both in composing and decomposing shapes, discussed in the previous section, and in comparing areas in specific contexts. For example, paper-folding activities lend themselves not just to explorations of symmetry but also to equal-area congruent parts. Some students can compare the area of two pieces of paper by cutting and overlaying them. Such experiences provide only initial development of area concepts, but these key foundations are important for later learning.

Volume

The volume of a 3D shape is a measure of the amount of material or space enclosed within the shape (see figure 3.18). A sophisticated conception of volume requires even more complexity than area. Adding a third dimension presents a significant challenge to students' spatial structuring—students will eventually need to extend thinking of rows and columns to include layers.

Volume can also involve liquids or solids. This leads to two ways to measure volume, illustrated by "packing" a space such as a three-dimensional array with cubic units and "filling" with iterations of a fluid unit that takes the shape of the container. For filling, the unit structure may be psychologically one-dimensional for many first graders. For example, students may simply "read off" the measure on a graduated cylinder. So students can compare the volume of two containers in at least two ways. They might pour each into a graduated cylinder to compare the measures. Or they might practice indirect comparison using transitive reasoning by using a third container to compare the volumes of the two containers. Students also can lay a foundation for later "packing" volume by filling containers (into which cubes fit well) with cubes.

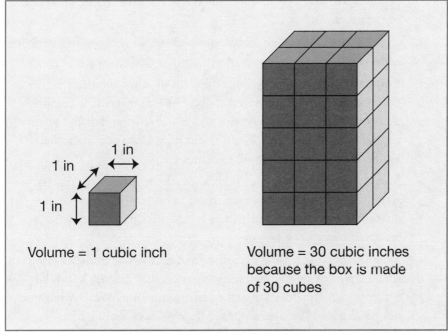

Volume = 1 cubic inch

Volume = 30 cubic inches because the box is made of 30 cubes

Fig. 3.18. The volume of an object is the number of unit cubes it takes to make or fill the object completely.

Geometry, Spatial Reasoning, and Measurement: Final Words

Geometric and spatial experiences are appropriate for, and achievable by, primary-grade students. High-quality activities are also highly motivating to first graders. Formal evaluations reveal that such activities contribute to students' development of both numerical and spatial/geometric concepts. Curricula that include substantial spatial and geometric activities show remarkably positive results. Students gain in geometric and spatial skills and show pronounced benefits in the areas of arithmetic and other areas in primary school. Students are better prepared for all school tasks when they gain the thinking tools and representational competence of geometric and spatial sense.

What if time is limited? What is most important? All the geometry and measurement content presented here is important and helpful for students and will prepare them for future learning. However, if your students enter first grade with little previous experience, or if your time for mathematics is limited, consider the following guidelines.

- Geometry and measurement activities—from deciding if a "very long, upside down" shape is truly a triangle to analyzing someone's map—are excellent contexts for mathematical reasoning, communication, and problem solving. These should be valued goals alongside the learning of concepts and skills.

- Recognize that most spatial relations can be taught and practiced throughout the day, integrated into daily activities both in and outside of school. However, they also should be addressed intentionally and explicitly through targeted tasks within those activities. Separate activities, such as making maps and models, are of secondary importance.

- Concentrate on the core knowledge and skills in shapes and structure and especially compositions and decompositions in space.

- Emphasize the spatial relations inherent in other geometry activities, such as those emphasized above. For example, shape compositions can develop spatial visualization. "Close your eyes and picture a square. Make one straight cut to cut it into two congruent halves. What did you get? What other shapes are possible?"

- Measurement concepts and skills also may be developed in other activities throughout the day. Any time comparing, ordering, or quantifying continuous quantities is called for in any subject area, measurement can be taught.

- Spend the available time extending and enhancing students' knowledge instead of simply reviewing concepts they already know. For example, students may know the terms *square* and *rectangle* but may not yet explicitly recognize that each must have four right angles ("square corners") and often do not understand that a square is also a rectangle because it has four right angles.

- When possible, connect geometry and measurement ideas with number ideas for mutual reinforcement of the ideas. For example, addition and subtraction problems arise naturally in contexts of measurement and of composing and decomposing shapes: "How many triangles did you use to fill the hexagon yesterday? So you have put together two triangles already. How many more triangles will you need to fill the hexagon with triangles?" and "This ribbon is fifteen inches long. When we cut off a piece that is eight inches long, how long will the leftover piece be?"

4 Mathematizing: Solving Problems, Reasoning, and Communicating, Connecting, and Representing Ideas in First Grade

The general processes of problem solving, reasoning, and communicating, connecting, and representing ideas are important at every grade level and in all topics in mathematics. To make sense of mathematics and to connect mathematics to the world around them, students at all levels must actively think about mathematical ideas and seek to connect the ideas to their existing knowledge. To extend their knowledge, students at all levels must solve new problems, and they must discuss their solution strategies and ideas with others so that they can examine and refine those strategies and ideas. Teachers are important in these processes because they can set expectations about mathematics: that mathematics is a sense-making enterprise, that discussing and explaining our reasoning and ideas are important for learning, and that mathematizing the world around us by examining everyday experiences from a mathematical point of view helps us understand both the world and mathematics better. Teachers can give children stimulating and enjoyable mathematical activities and problems in a nurturing math-talk environment that not only develops children's mathematical thinking but also satisfies children's curiosity, their eagerness to explore and learn, and their desire to engage with their peers and with adults.

In addition to these general processes of representing, reasoning, communicating, connecting, and problem solving, specific mathematical reasoning processes also exist that are important across all topics in mathematics and that mathematics instruction should help children develop. These are—

- unitizing—finding or creating a unit, such as seeing one hundred as ten groups of ten or joining shapes to make a house shape and then repeating the house shape to show a village;

- decomposing and composing, such as decomposing 17 into 1 ten and 7 ones or finding two different ways to make a large shape from smaller shapes;

- relating and ordering, such as knowing that eighty-three beads is more than sixty-seven beads because the eighties come after the sixties or because 8 tens are more than 6 tens, or determining that one birdhouse is taller than another by measuring both; and

- looking for patterns and structures and organizing information, such as noticing a pattern in pairs of numbers that have the same sum: as one addend increases, the other decreases; noticing that 2 + 7 is the same as 7 + 2; and noticing that opposite sides of rectangles are always the same length.

Examples of such processes have been given in this book for number and geometry. It is vital for parents and teachers to support children in using these mathematical processes.

Throughout this book we have provided snapshots of worthwhile activities for first-grade children and some snippets of conversations to illustrate how you might engage children to extend their thinking and draw out mathematical ideas. We end with the suggestion that you revisit some of the examples given here, as well as some activities and environments that you already provide your students, and reconsider these activities with an eye toward engaging children in mathematical processes. Consider how you might further mathematize those activities and environments and enhance your classroom math talk to encourage reasoning, communicating, connecting and representing mathematical ideas, and problem solving. Think about where you can help children unitize, decompose and compose, relate and order, look for and describe patterns and structures, and organize mathematical information. As you do so, consider seeking opportunities throughout the day for the following:

- Promote unitizing by drawing children's attention to things that are organized into units, such as juice boxes that are packaged together or eggs packaged in a carton, and to things that are organized into repeated units, such as the repeated design in a wallpaper pattern or the two identical parts in a symmetrical design.

- Encourage children to reason about how many objects are in a collection of objects grouped into bundles of tens and some ones.

- Encourage children to reason about how many objects there are in all when you hide a known number of objects and then put one or a few more objects out in view (to promote counting on).

- Ask children to compare collections and encourage reasoning about which has more or less and how much more or how much less.

- Provide opportunities for children to explore how to combine and take apart shapes or collections of things, and encourage children to discuss and reason about the process.

- Draw children's attention to features, attributes, and sizes of shapes and objects, including their edges, corners, and faces, and discuss how aspects of objects affect such things as whether they roll, stack, or fit in a space.

Most of all, we encourage you to make learning the important mathematical ideas of grade 1 active, engaging, and stimulating, for your students as well as for you.

References

Chapter 1

Donovan, M. Suzanne, and John D. Bransford, eds. *How Students Learn: Mathematics in the Classroom.* Washington, D.C.: National Academy Press, 2005.

Fuson, Karen, and Aki Murata. "Integrating NRC Principles and the NCTM Process Standards to Form a Class Learning Path Model That Individualizes within Whole-Class Activities." *National Council of Supervisors of Mathematics Journal of Mathematics Education Leadership* 10, no. 1 (2007): 72–91.

Kilpatrick, Jeremy, Jane Swafford, and Bradford Findell, eds. *Adding It Up: Helping Children Learn Mathematics.* National Research Council, Mathematics Learning Study Committee, Center for Education, Division of Behavioral and Social Sciences and Education. Washington, D.C.: National Academy Press, 2001.

National Council of Teachers of Mathematics (NCTM). *Focus in Kindergarten.* Reston, Va.: NCTM, 2010.

———. *Curriculum Focal Points for Prekindergarten through Grade 8 Mathematics: A Quest for Coherence.* Reston, Va.: NCTM, 2006.

———. *Principles and Standards for School Mathematics.* Reston, Va.: NCTM, 2000.

———. *Curriculum and Evaluation Standards for School Mathematics.* Reston, Va.: NCTM, 1989.

Chapter 2

Baroody, Arthur J., and Ronald T. Coslick. *Fostering Children's Mathematical Power.* Mahwah, N.J.: Lawrence Erlbaum Associates, 1998.

Carpenter, Thomas P., Elizabeth Fennema, Megan L. Franke, Linda Levi, and Susan B. Empson. *Children's Mathematics: Cognitively Guided Instruction.* Portsmouth, N.H.: Heinemann, 1999.

Clements, Douglas H. "Subitizing: What Is It? Why Teach It?" *Teaching Children Mathematics* 5 (1999): 400–405.

Clements, Douglas H., and Julie Sarama. "Early Childhood Mathematics Learning." In *Second Handbook of Research on Mathematics Teaching and Learning,* edited by Frank K. Lester, Jr., pp. 461–555. New York: Information Age Publishing, 2007.

———. "Experimental Evaluation of a Research-Based Preschool Mathematics Curriculum." *American Educational Research Journal* 45 (2008): 443–94.

Cross, Christopher T., Taniesha A. Woods, and Heidi Schweingruber, eds. *Mathematics Learning in Early Childhood: Paths toward Excellence and Equity.* National Research Council, Center for Education, Division of Behavioral and Social Sciences and Education. Washington, D.C.: National Academy Press, 2009.

Fuson, Karen C. "Research on Learning and Teaching Addition and Subtraction of Whole Numbers." In *The Analysis of Arithmetic for Mathematics Teaching,* edited by Gaea Leinhardt, Ralph T. Putnam, and Rosemary A. Hattrup, pp. 53–187. Hillsdale, N.J.: Lawrence Erlbaum Associates, 1992a.

———. "Research on Whole Number Addition and Subtraction." In *Handbook of Research on Mathematics Teaching and Learning,* edited by Douglas Grouws, pp. 243–75. New York: Macmillan, 1992b.

———. *Math Expressions.* Boston: Houghton Mifflin Co., 2006, 2009.

Kilpatrick, Jeremy, Jane Swafford, and Bradford Findell, eds. *Adding It Up: Helping Children Learn Mathematics.* Washington, D.C.: National Academy Press, 2001.

National Council of Teachers of Mathematics (NCTM). *Focus in Prekindergarten.* Reston, Va.: NCTM, 2009.

———. *Focus in Kindergarten.* Reston, Va.: NCTM, 2010.

———. *Focus in Grade 2.* Reston, Va.: NCTM, forthcoming.

Piaget, Jean. *The Child's Conception of Number.* New York: W. W. Norton & Co., 1941/1965.